WrestleMania 25th Anniversary

EXTREME RULES MATCH
MATT HARDY VS JEFF HARDY

MATCH
PAGES 56-61

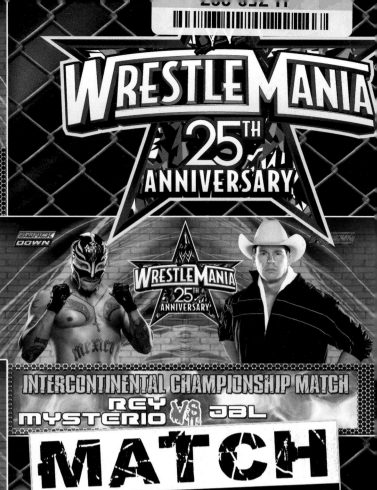

INTERCONTINENTAL CHAMPIONSHIP MATCH
REY MYSTERIO VS JBL

MATCH
PAGES 66-71

UNDERTAKER VS SHAWN MICHAELS

MATCH
PAGES 78-83

TRIPLE TREAT MATCH
EDGE VS BIG SHOW VS JOHN CENA

MATCH
PAGES 88-93

WWE CHAMPIONSHIP MATCH
TRIPLE H VS RANDY ORTON

MATCH
PAGES 102-107

Pedigree®

Published by Pedigree Books, Beech Hill House, Walnut Gardens, Exeter, Devon EX4 4DH. Email: books@pedigreegroup.co.uk

Web: www.pedigreebooks.com

£7.99

MATCH CARD

Tito Santana def. The Executioner

David Sammartino w/ Bruno Sammartino vs Brutus 'The Barber' Beefcake w/ Luscious Johnny Valiant
went to a double-DQ

Ricky 'The Dragon' Steamboat def. Matt Borne

King Kong Bundy w/ Jimmy Hart def. Special Delivery Jones

Bodyslam Challenge
Andre the Giant def. Big John Studd

Intercontinental Championship Match
Junkyard Dog def. Greg 'The Hammer' Valentine w/ Jimmy Hart via count-out

World Tag Team Championship Match
Nikolai Volkoff and Iron Sheik w/ Classy Freddie Blassie def. Mike Rotundo and Barry Windham
to become new champions

Women's Championship Match
Wendi Richter w/ Cyndi Lauper def. Leilani Kai w/ Fabulous Moolah to become new champion

Main Event
Hulk Hogan and Mr. T w/ 'Superfly' Jimmy Snuka def. 'Rowdy' Roddy Piper and 'Mr. Wonderful' Paul Orndorff
w/ Cowboy Bob Orton

DID YOU KNOW...

The night before WrestleMania, Hulk Hogan and Mr. T hosted an episode of Saturday Night Live to help promote the event.

The event was viewed by more than one million fans through closed circuit television, making it the largest event on CCTV in the United States at the time.

WRESTLEMANIA®

MATCH CARD

'Mr. Wonderful' Paul Orndorff vs 'Magnificent' Don Muraco w/ Mr. Fuji went to a double countout

Intercontinental Championship Match
Randy 'Macho Man' Savage w/ Elizabeth def. George 'The Animal' Steele to retain his Championship

Jake 'The Snake' Roberts def. George Wells

Boxing Match
Mr. T w/ Joe Frazier and the Haiti Kid def. 'Rowdy' Roddy Piper w/ Cowboy Bob Orton by DQ

Women's Championship Match
Fabulous Moolah def. Velvet McIntyre to become new champion

Flag Match
Corporal Kirchner def. Nikolai Volkoff w/ Classy Freddie Blassie

WWE and NFL Battle Royal
Andre the Giant def. Jimbo Covert (Chicago Bears), Pedro Morales, Tony Atlas, Ted Arcidi, Harvey Martin (Dallas Cowboys), Dan Spivey, Hillbilly Jim, King Tonga, Iron Sheik, Ernie Holmes (Pittsburgh Steelers), Big John Studd, B. Brian Blair, Jumpin' Jim Brunzell, Bill Fralic (Atlanta Falcons), Bret 'Hit Man' Hart, Jim 'The Anvil' Neidhart, Russ Francis (San Francisco 49ers), Bruno Sammartino and William 'Refrigerator' Perry (Chicago Bears)

World Tag Team Championship Match
British Bulldogs w/ Captain Lou Albano and Ozzy Osbourne def. The Dream Team (Brutus Beefcake and Greg 'The Hammer' Valentine), w/ Luscious Johnny Valiant to become new champions

Ricky 'The Dragon' Steamboat def. Hercules

'Adorable' Adrian Adonis w/ Jimmy Hart def. Uncle Elmer

Terry and Hoss Funk w/ Jimmy Hart def. Tito Santana and Junkyard Dog

Steel Cage Match for the WWE Championship
Hulk Hogan def. King Kong Bundy w/ Bobby 'The Brain' Heenan to retain

DID YOU KNOW...
In one of the three main events at *WrestleMania 2*, Hulk Hogan defeated King Kong Bundy in the only Steel Cage Match in WrestleMania history.

WrestleMania 2 was staged in three different cities – New York, Los Angeles and Chicago – and featured a Triple Main Event.

LUMBERJACK MATCH FOR THE UNIFIED TAG TEAM CHAMPIONSHIP

CARLITO™ & PRIMO™ vs THE MIZ™ & JOHN MORRISON™

"Well here we are! *WrestleMania XXV!* Twenty five years in the making! And what a match to kick off proceedings!"

"And making their way to ring are The Miz and John Morrison!"

"Here come the Lumberjacks who could play an important part in this match to unify the WWE and World Tag Team Championships!"

"These two young athletes have revolutionised the tag team division in WWE."

"John Morrison looks supremely confident. This is not his first appearance at *WrestleMania* and I am sure it won't be his last!"

"And here come their opponents. The two brothers from Puerto Rico, Carlito and Primo!"

"Carlito and Primo are taking their time making their way to the ring. Many of the Lumberjacks on the outside have had problems with the brothers Colon in the past!"

"The match is underway and it is The Miz and Carlito starting things off! Carlito catches The Miz with a big boot to the face!"

"Miz makes the tag to John Morrison and he is in complete control!"

"The Miz is back inside the ring and he and his partner are looking for a double team move here!"

"Carlito is slammed to the canvas face first! That is going to hurt in the morning!"

"Morrison and The Miz work so well together! Just look at this offence!"

"And Morrison and The Miz are not finished with him yet! What are they looking for here?"

"A double gut-buster from the World Tag Team Champions! Carlito is in real trouble here!"

"The Miz seems pretty proud of himself. He needs to keep his arrogance in check, a match like this can turn around very quickly."

"The Miz continues to work over Carlito. He has that rear chin lock locked in tight!"

"The Miz tags in his partner. Look at this! Carlito with a huge counter move! He needs to make the tag!"

"Primo is desperate for the tag. The Miz and Morrison have managed to keep him out of the match thus far!"

"Carlito makes the tag! But John Morrison catches Primo with a huge dropkick as he enters the ring! I think that may have hurt Morrison as well!"

"Primo is climbing to the top rope! He needs to keep an eye on those Lumberjacks on the outside!"

"Primo flies through the air and catches Morrison with a picture perfect flying crossbody block!"

"Primo has Morrison set up for the Backstabber! If he can connect with this move, the match could well be over!"

"Primo went for the pin but Morrison still had enough energy to kick out. Morrison sends Primo into the corner only to be met with a boot to the face!"

"Primo is going for the cover! 1...2...3! Primo makes the pin and wins the match!"

"Primo can not believe it! In his first appearance at *WrestleMania* he and his brother have unified the championships!"

"Carlito and Primo are now both the World and WWE Tag Team Champions!"

"I can not remember the last time one team held both championships! What an achievement for these second generation Superstars!"

"It looked at one stage that Carlito may have been completely out of it but his younger brother made the save and added more gold to Carlito's already impressive trophy cabinet!"

"There have been some great "Brothers" tag teams in the history of WWE, but I really feel that these young men have the potential to dominate the division for years to come!"

"There will be some serious partying going on back home in the Caribbean tonight!"

No 25

THE LEGION OF DOOM™

Statistics...

Name: **Hawk**
Height: **6-foot-3**
Weight: **245 pounds**
From: **Chicago, IL**
Signature Move:
Doomsday Device

Name: **Animal**
Height: **6-foot-1**
Weight: **285 pounds**
From: **Chicago, IL**
Signature Move:
Doomsday Device

WrestleMania Record

March 24, 1991 – *WrestleMania VII:*
The Legion of Doom defeated Power and Glory in 59 seconds.

April 5, 1992 – *WrestleMania VIII:*
The Legion of Doom brought Paul Ellering back to the WWE to manage them.

March 23, 1997 – *WrestleMania XIII:*
Ahmed Johnson and Legion of Doom defeated The Nation of Domination in a Chicago Street Fight.

BIG BOSSMAN™

No 24

WrestleMania Record

April 2, 1989 – *WrestleMania V:*
The Twin Towers (Big Boss Man and Akeem) def. The Rockers (Marty Jannetty and Shawn Michaels).

April 1, 1990 – *WrestleMania VI:*
Big Bossman def. Akeem.

March 24, 1991 – *WrestleMania VII:*
Big Bossman def. Mr. Perfect (Intercontinental Champion) by DQ.

April 5, 1992 – *WrestleMania VIII:*
"Hacksaw" Jim Duggan, Sgt.Slaughter, Virgil and Big Bossman defeated The Mountie, Repo Man and The Nasty Boys.

March 28, 1999 – *WrestleMania XV:*
Undertaker def. Big Bossman in a Hell in a Cell match.

April 2, 2000 – *WrestleMania 2000:*
Big Bossman & Bull Buchanan def. The Godfather & D-Lo Brown.

Statistics...

Name: **Big Bossman**
Height: **6-foot-6**
Weight: **315 pounds**
From: **Cobb County, GA**
Signature Move:
Sidewalk Slam

THE BIG WRESTLEMANIA
QUIZ PART I

WrestleMania is the biggest event in the world of sports entertainment, but how much do you know about the history of this incredible spectacle? Throughout this annual you will find 70 questions on *WrestleMania's* past and present. Add up your scores along the way and see which Championship you win at the end!

Q1. In what year did the first *WrestleMania* take place?

A. 1990 ☐
B. 1985 ☐
C. 1984 ☐

Q2. Who was the first Superstar to set foot in the ring at *WrestleMania?*

A. King Kong Bundy ☐
B. Tito Santana ☐
C. Hulk Hogan ☐

Q3. Who did Hulk Hogan team with at *WrestleMania?*

A. Mr. T ☐
B. Roddy Piper ☐
C. Paul Orndorff ☐

Q4. Which Superstar competed for the Intercontinental Championship at *WrestleMania 2?*

A. George 'The Animal' Steel ☐
B. Earthquake ☐
C. Mr Perfect ☐

Q5. Who won the WWE/NFL Battle Royal at *WrestleMania 2?*

A. Hulk Hogan ☐
B. Ultimate Warrior ☐
C. Andre The Giant ☐

Q6. Who did Hulk Hogan face for the World Championship at *WrestleMania 2?*

A. Randy 'Macho Man' Savage ☐
B. King Kong Bundy ☐
C. Andre The Giant ☐

Q7. Who won the Intercontinental Championship at *WrestleMania III?*

A. Ultimate Warrior ☐
B. Ricky Steamboat ☐
C. Undertaker ☐

Q8. What was special about the match between Rowdy Roddy Piper and Adrian Adonis at *WrestleMania III?*

A. Loser had head shaved ☐
B. Loser left WWE ☐
C. Ladder Match ☐

Q9. Who faced Junkyard Dog at *WrestleMania III?*

A. Ric Flair ☐
B. Harley Race ☐
C. Rick Martel ☐

Q10. Who is this WWE Legend that accompanied Andre The Giant to the ring at *WrestleMania III?*

A. Jimmy Hart ☐
B. Bobby 'The Brain' Heenan ☐
C. Classie Freddie Blassie ☐

13

MARCH 29, 1987

WF®

Title: 'Bigger, Badder & Better'
Location: Pontiac, MI
Arena: Pontiac SilverDome
Attendance: 93,173

WrestleMania III

MATCH CARD

Can Am Connection def. Cowboy Bob Orton and Magnificent Muraco

Full Nelson Challenge
Billy Jack Haynes vs Hercules went to a double count-out

Hillbilly Jim, Little Beaver and The Haiti Kid def. King Kong Bundy, Lord Littlebrook and Little Tokyo by DQ
when Bundy flattened Little Beaver

"Loser Must Bow" Match
King Harley Race w/ Bobby 'The Brain' Heenan and Fabulous Moolah def. Junkyard Dog

The Dream Team (Brutus Beefcake and Greg 'The Hammer' Valentine), w/ Luscious Johnny Valiant and Dino Bravo
def. The Rougeau Brothers

Hair vs. Hair Match
'Rowdy' Roddy Piper def. 'Adorable' Adrian Adonis w/ Jimmy Hart

Hart Foundation and 'Dangerous' Danny Davis w/ Jimmy Hart def. British Bulldogs and Tito Santana

'The Natural' Butch Reed def. Koko B. Ware

Intercontinental Championship Match
Ricky 'The Dragon' Steamboat w/ George 'The Animal' Steele def. Randy 'Macho Man' Savage w/ Elizabeth
to become new champion

Honky Tonk Man w/ Jimmy Hart def. Jake 'The Snake' Roberts w/ Alice Cooper

Nikolai Volkoff and Iron Sheik def. Killer Bees by DQ

WWE Championship Match
Hulk Hogan def. Andre the Giant w/ Bobby 'The Brain' Heenan to retain

DID YOU KNOW...

93,173 people packed the Pontiac Silverdome for *WrestleMania III*, the largest indoor attendance for any event in WWE history.

Aretha Franklin kicked off *WrestleMania III* with her rendition of *America the Beautiful*

MATCH CARD

Battle Royal
Bad News Brown def. Bret 'Hit Man' Hart, Jim 'The Anvil' Neidhart, Jim Powers, Paul Roma, Sika, 'Dangerous' Danny Davis, Sam Houston, Hillbilly Jim, B. Brian Blair, Jumpin' Jim Brunzell, Ray Rougeau, Jacques Rougeau, Junkyard Dog, Ken Patera, Ron Bass, King Harley Race, Nikolai Volkoff, Boris Zukov and George 'The Animal' Steele

Ultimate Warrior def. Hercules w/ Bobby 'The Brain' Heenan

Intercontinental Championship Match
Brutus 'The Barber' Beefcake def. Honky Tonk Man w/ Jimmy Hart and Peggy Sue by DQ

The Islanders and Bobby 'The Brain' Heenan def. British Bulldogs and Koko B. Ware w/ Matilda

World Tag Team Championship Match
Demolition w/ Mr. Fuji def. Strike Force to become new champions

World Championship Tournament
Round One Match – 'Million Dollar Man' Ted DiBiase w/ Virgil and Andre the Giant def. Hacksaw Jim Duggan

Round One Match – Don Muraco w/ 'Superstar' Billy Graham def. Dino Bravo w/ Frenchy Martin by DQ

Round One Match – Greg 'The Hammer' Valentine w/ Jimmy Hart def. Ricky 'The Dragon' Steamboat

Round One Match – Randy 'Macho Man' Savage w/ Elizabeth def. 'The Natural' Butch Reed w/ Slick

Round One Match – One Man Gang w/ Slick def. Bam Bam Bigelow w/ Oliver Humperdink by count-out

Round One Match – 'Ravishing' Rick Rude w/ Bobby 'The Brain' Heenan vs Jake 'The Snake' Roberts went to a draw

Round Two Match – Hulk Hogan vs Andre the Giant w/ Bobby 'The Brain' Heenan, 'Million Dollar Man' Ted DiBiase and Virgil ended in a double DQ

Round Two Match – 'Million Dollar Man' Ted DiBiase w/ Virgil def. Don Muraco w/ 'Superstar' Billy Graham

Round Two Match – Randy 'Macho Man' Savage w/ Elizabeth def. Greg 'The Hammer' Valentine w/ Jimmy Hart

Round Three Match – Randy 'Macho Man' Savage w/ Elizabeth def. One Man Gang w/ Slick by DQ

WWE Championship Tournament Final Match
Randy 'Macho Man' Savage w/ Elizabeth and Hulk Hogan def. 'Million Dollar Man' Ted DiBiase w/ Virgil and Andre the Giant to become new champion

DID YOU KNOW...

WrestleMania IV had 15 matches, the most of any *WrestleMania* event.

WrestleMania IV was the first time a new WWE Champion was crowned at *WrestleMania*, when Randy Savage won the vacant title.

No 23

BIG JOHN STUDD™

Statistics...

Name:
Big John Studd

Height:
6-foot-10

Weight:
364 pounds

From:
Los Angeles, CA

Signature Move:
Reverse Bear Hug,
Backbreaker

WrestleMania Record

March 31, 1985 – *WrestleMania:*
Andre The Giant def. Big John Studd in a
special $15,000 Body Slam challenge.
April 5, 1986 – *WrestleMania 2:*
Andre The Giant won a huge battle royal
which featured Big John Studd and
several NFL football players.
April 2, 1989 – *WrestleMania V:*
Jake 'The Snake' Roberts def. Andre
The Giant with Big John Studd acting as
special guest referee.
March 14, 2004 – *WrestleMania XX:*
Big John Studd was honoured with all the
other Hall of Fame inductees during the
pay-per-view event.

THE HONKY TONK MAN™

No 22

WrestleMania Record

March 29, 1987 – *WrestleMania III:*
The Honky Tonk Man def. Jake 'The
Snake' Roberts.

March 27, 1988 – *WrestleMania IV:*
Brutus 'The Barber' Beefcake def.
Intercontinental Champion Honky Tonk
Man w/Jimmy Hart and Peggy Sue by DQ.

April 2, 1989 – *WrestleMania V:*
The Hart Foundation def. The Honky Tonk
Man and Greg Valentine.

Statistics...

Name:
The Honky Tonk Man

Height:
6-foot-1

Weight:
271 pounds

From:
Memphis, TN

Signature Move:
Shake, Rattle & Roll

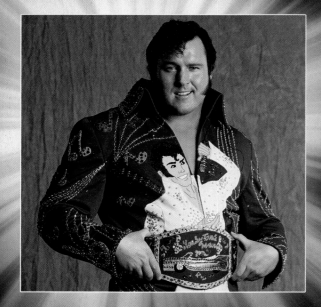

THE BIG
WRESTLEMANIA
QUIZ PART II

How do you think you scored in the first round? Are you ready for the next challenge?

Q11. Who won the Battle Royal at *WrestleMania IV?*

A. Bad News Brown ☐
B. Bret 'Hit Man' Hart ☐
C. Andre The Giant ☐

Q12. Who faced Honky Tonk Man at *WrestleMania IV?*

A. Ultimate Warrior ☐
B. Brutus 'The Barber' Beefcake ☐
C. Jerry 'The King' Lawler ☐

Q13. Who won the Intercontinental Championship at *WrestleMania V?*

A. Ultimate Warrior ☐
B. 'Ravishing' Rick Rude ☐
C. Honky Tonk Man ☐

Q14. Who is this Superstar that won the WWE Championship at *WrestleMania IV?*

A. Randy "Macho Man" Savage ☐
B. Hercules ☐
C. Dino Bravo ☐

Q15. Who defeated Bobby 'The Brain' Heenan in just 32 seconds at *WrestleMania V?*

A. The Red Rooster ☐
B. Tito Santana ☐
C. Rick Martel ☐

Q16. Which current WWE Superstar made his *WrestleMania* debut at *WrestleMania V?*

A. Triple H ☐
B. Undertaker ☐
C. Shawn Michaels ☐

Q17. What was special about the location of *WrestleMania VI?*

A. First in Canada ☐
B. First to be outside ☐
C. Multiple locations ☐

Q18. Who made up the tag team called The Colossal Connection?

A. Haku & Hulk Hogan ☐
B. Haku & Akeem ☐
C. Haku & Andre The Giant ☐

Q19. Who won the World Tag Team Championship at *WrestleMania VI?*

A. The Steiner Brothers ☐
B. The Heavenly Bodies ☐
C. Demolition ☐

Q20. Who is this Superstar that unified the WWE Championship and the Intercontinental Championship at *WrestleMania VI?*

A. Hulk Hogan ☐
B. Ultimate Warrior ☐
C. The Renegade ☐

APRIL 2, 1989

Title: 'The Megapowers Explode'
Location: Atlantic City, NJ
Arena: Trump Plaza
Convention Centre
Attendance: 18,946

WWF WRESTLEMANIA V

MATCH CARD

Hercules def. King Haku w/ Bobby 'The Brain' Heenan

The Twin Towers w/ Slick def. The Rockers

'Million Dollar Man' Ted DiBiase w/ Virgil vs Brutus 'The Barber' Beefcake ended in a double count-out

The Bushwhackers def. The Rougeau Brothers w/ Jimmy Hart

Mr. Perfect def. The Blue Blazer

Handicap Match for the World Tag Team Championship
Demolition def. Powers of Pain and Mr Fuji to retain

Dino Bravo w/ Frenchy Martin def. 'Rugged' Ronnie Garvin

The Brain Busters w/ Bobby 'The Brain' Heenan def. Strike Force

Jake 'The Snake' Roberts def. Andre the Giant w/ Bobby 'The Brain' Heenan by DQ
(Big John Studd was special guest referee)

The Hart Foundation def. Rhythm & Blues (Honky Tonk Man and Greg 'The Hammer' Valentine), w/ Jimmy Hart

Intercontinental Championship Match
'Ravishing' Rick Rude w/ Bobby 'The Brain' Heenan def. Ultimate Warrior to become new champion

Bad News Brown vs Hacksaw Jim Duggan went to a no contest

The Red Rooster def. Bobby 'The Brain' Heenan

WWE Championship Match
Hulk Hogan def. Randy 'Macho Man' Savage w/ Elizabeth in a neutral corner to become new champion

DID YOU KNOW...
Both Shawn Michaels and the Big Boss Man made their *WrestleMania* debuts at *WrestleMania V*.

Rap superstars Run D.M.C. performed a special *WrestleMania* rap at *WrestleMania V*.

APRIL 1, 1990

WrestleMania VI

MATCH CARD

'The Model' Rick Martel def. Koko B. Ware

World Tag Team Championship Match
Demolition def. Colossal Connection w/ Bobby 'The Brain' Heenan to become new champions

Earthquake w/ Jimmy Hart def. Hercules

Brutus 'The Barber' Beefcake def. Mr. Perfect w/ The Genius

'Rowdy' Roddy Piper vs Bad News Brown went to a no contest

The Hart Foundation def. The Bolsheviks

The Barbarian w/ Bobby 'The Brain' Heenan def. Tito Santana

Mixed Tag Team Match
Dusty Rhodes and Sapphire w/ Elizabeth def. Randy 'Macho King' Savage and Queen Sherri

The Orient Express w/ Mr. Fuji def. The Rockers by count-out

Hacksaw Jim Duggan def. Dino Bravo w/ Earthquake

Million Dollar Championship Match
'Million Dollar Man' Ted DiBiase w/ Virgil def. Jake 'The Snake' Roberts by count-out

Big Boss Man def. Akeem w/ Slick

'Ravishing' Rick Rude w/ Bobby 'The Brain' Heenan def. 'Superfly' Jimmy Snuka

Title vs. Title Match
Ultimate Warrior def. Hulk Hogan to retain Intercontinental Championship and become new WWE Champion

DID YOU KNOW...

For the first time in *WrestleMania* history, the main event of *WrestleMania VI* was a Title-for-Title match, as Intercontinental Champion Ultimate Warrior took on WWE Champion Hulk Hogan.

Hogan's loss in the main event of *WrestleMania VI* was his first *WrestleMania* loss ever.

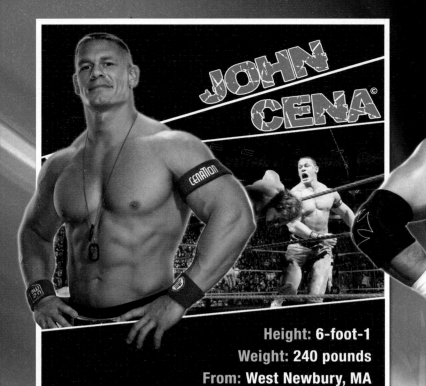

JOHN CENA

Height: 6-foot-1
Weight: 240 pounds
From: West Newbury, MA
Signature Move: Attitude Adjustment, STF

TRIPLE H

Height: 6-foot-4
Weight: 255 pounds
From: Greenwich, CT
Signature Move: Pedigree

RANDY ORTON

Height: 6-foot-4
Weight: 245 pounds
From: St Louis, MO
Signature Move: RKO

MATT HARDY

Height: 6-foot-2
Weight: 236 pounds
From: Cameron, NC
Signature Move: Twist of Fate

RAW

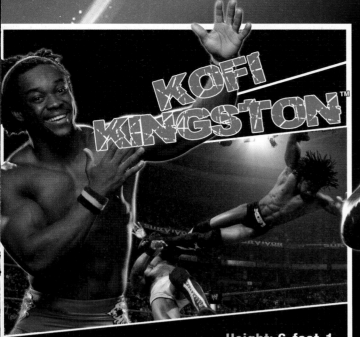

KOFI KINGSTON™

Height: **6-foot-1**
Weight: **200 pounds**
From: **Jamaica**
Signature Move: **Cool Runnings**

BIG SHOW®

Height: **7-foot-0**
Weight: **441 pounds**
From: **Tampa, FL**
Signature Move: **Chokeslam**

SHAWN MICHAELS©

Height: **6-foot-1**
Weight: **225 pounds**
From: **San Antonio, TX**
Signature Move: **Sweet Chin Music**

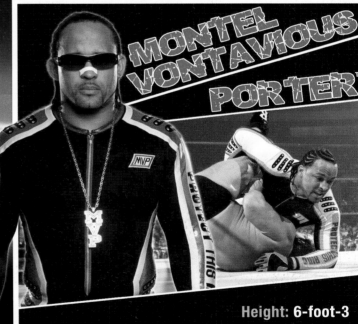

MONTEL VONTAVIOUS PORTER™

Height: **6-foot-3**
Weight: **249 pounds**
From: **Miami, FL**
Signature Move: **The Playmaker**

PROFILES

No 21 GREG 'THE HAMMER' VALENTINE ™

Statistics...

Name:
Greg 'The Hammer' Valentine

Height:
6-foot-0

Weight:
243 pounds

From:
Seattle, WA

Signature Move:
Figure-Four Leglock

WrestleMania Record

April 7, 1986 – *WrestleMania 2:* The Dream Team (Brutus Beefcake & Greg Valentine) was def. by the British Bulldogs for the World Tag Team Championship.

March 29, 1987 – *WrestleMania III:* The Dream Team, w/ Luscious Johnny Valiant and Dino Bravo def. The Rougeau Brothers.

March 27, 1988 – *WrestleMania IV:* Greg 'The Hammer' Valentine w/ Jimmy Hart def. Ricky 'The Dragon' Steamboat.

March 27, 1988 – *WrestleMania IV:* Randy 'Macho Man' Savage w/ Elizabeth def. Greg 'The Hammer' Valentine w/ Jimmy Hart.

April 2, 1989 – *WrestleMania V:* The Hart Foundation def. Honky Tonk Man and Greg 'The Hammer' Valentine w/ Jimmy Hart.

March 24, 1991 – *WrestleMania VII:* Earthquake def. Greg 'The Hammer' Valentine.

March 14, 2004 - *WrestleMania XX:* Greg Valentine was honoured with all the other Hall of Fame inductees during the pay-per-view.

JAKE 'THE SNAKE' ROBERTS ™ No 20

WrestleMania Record

April 2, 1986 – *WrestleMania 2:* Jake 'The Snake' Roberts def. ex-football player George Wells.

March 29, 1987 – *WrestleMania III:* Honky Tonk Man w/Jimmy Hart def. Jake 'The Snake' Roberts (with rock star Alice Cooper).

March 27, 1988 – *WrestleMania IV:* Jake 'The Snake' Roberts & Rick Rude wrestle to a 15 minute draw in the 1st round of the WWE Championship Tournament.

April 2, 1989 – *WrestleMania V:* Jake 'The Snake' Roberts def. Andre the Giant by DQ when Andre attacked guest referee Big John Studd.

April 1, 1990 – *WrestleMania VI:* Ted DiBiase def. Jake 'The Snake' Roberts by count out to win the Million Dollar Championship.

March 24, 1991 – *WrestleMania VII:* Jake 'The Snake' Roberts def. Rick Martel in a Blind Fold Match.

April 5, 1992 – *WrestleMania VIII:* Undertaker def. Jake 'The Snake' Roberts.

March 31, 1996 – *WrestleMania XII:* Owen Hart, British Bulldog & Vader def. Jake 'The Snake' Roberts, Ahmed Johnson & Yokozuna

Statistics...

Name:
Jake 'The Snake' Roberts

Height:
6-foot-5

Weight:
261 pounds

From:
Stone Mountain, GA

Signature Move:
DDT

THE BIG WRESTLEMANIA QUIZ PART III

You've made it to round three of the *WrestleMania* Quiz! How are you doing so far? Don't forget to keep a tally of your score and see which Championship you have won at the end of the quiz!

Q21. From which city did *WrestleMania VII* emanate?

A. Los Angeles ☐
B. New York ☐
C. Baltimore ☐

Q22. Who won the World Tag Team Championship at *WrestleMania VII?*

A. The Natural Disasters ☐
B. The Nasty Boys ☐
C. The Rock & Roll Express ☐

Q23. Who did Undertaker face at *WrestleMania VII?*

A. Kane ☐
B. 'Superfly' Jimmy Snuka ☐
C. Hulk Hogan ☐

Q24. Who is this Superstar that defeated Tito Santana at *WrestleMania VIII?*

A. Marty Jannetty ☐
B. Jeff Hardy ☐
C. Shawn Michaels ☐

Q25. The Natural Disasters were made up of which two Superstars?

A. Plague and Tsunami ☐
B. Typhoon and Famine ☐
C. Earthquake & Typhoon ☐

Q26. Who was defeated by Owen Hart at *WrestleMania VIII?*

A. Skinner ☐
B. Gillberg ☐
C. Bret 'Hit Man' Hart ☐

Q27. Who won the first match at *WrestleMania IX?*

A. Shawn Michaels ☐
B. Tatanka ☐
C. Mr Perfect ☐

Q28. Who did Undertaker face at *WrestleMania IX?*

A. Giant Gonzales ☐
B. Andre The Giant ☐
C. The Great Khali ☐

Q29. How many times did the WWE Championship change hands at *WrestleMania IX?*

A. Once ☐
B. Twice ☐
C. Three times ☐

Q30. Who is this Superstar that shocked the world by winning the WWE Championship at *WrestleMania IX?*

A. Hulk Hogan ☐
B. Bret 'Hit Man' Hart ☐
C. Mr. Fuji ☐

Answers – 21-A, 22-B, 23-B, 24-C, 25-C, 26-A, 27-B, 28-A, 29-B, 30-A

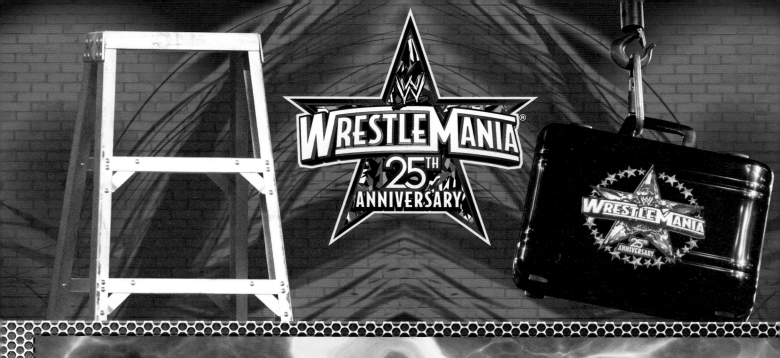

MONEY IN THE BANK LADDER MATCH

"Now we are about to see one of the most exciting matches in the whole WWE. The Money in the Bank Ladder Match!"

"And here you see last year's winner of the match, CM Punk, making his way to the ring!"

"One Superstar who will want to stop CM Punk from winning the match two years running is this man, Mark Henry!"

"And here comes the United States Champion, Montel Vontavious Porter, better known as MVP."

"Look at this! Finlay and his son, Hornswoggle! Finlay is no stranger to a hardcore environment!"

"Here comes Shelton Benjamin, one of the best pure athletes in WWE today. And again, Benjamin is no stranger to the ladder match!"

"Making his *WrestleMania* debut, here is Kofi Kingston! Kingston looks really pumped up tonight!"

"The newly-acquired ECW Superstar, Christian, makes his way down to the ring for his first *WrestleMania* match since returning to WWE just a few months ago."

"And finally, here comes the last man in the match, the always dangerous, Kane!"

"The match is underway and immediately Kofi Kingston uses his incredible vertical leap to legdrop the ladder right into the faces of his opponents!"

"Five of the Superstars involved in this match are just inches away from grabbing the briefcase and winning the match here!"

"But look at that! The two largest Superstars in the ring, Kane and Mark Henry, just sent them all crashing to the canvas below."

"Finlay delivers a brutal dropkick to the side of Mark Henry's head!"

"Finlay and Kane are on the outside! Christian just flew from the top rope and took out both men!"

"Oh My God! CM Punk and Kofi Kingston with a double suicide dive to the outside take everybody out!"

"Shelton Benjamin must be insane! Look at the height of that ladder!"

"Benjamin may be looking to create a *WrestleMania* moment here! Don't do it Shelton! Shelton Benjamin just leapt from a thirty foot ladder! Did you hear that impact?"

"Finlay and Mark Henry are in the ring and Finlay just nailed Henry with the shillelagh! That is perfectly legal in this match!"

"Hornswoggle is in the ring with his own Hornswoggle-sized step ladder!"

"Hornswoggle just launched himself from Mark Henry and has taken everyone out with a giant Tadpole Splash! This match is just incredible."

"Finlay has a chance to take advantage here. But Kofi Kingston just hit the Irishman with some creative offence!"

"Kofi Kingston scaled the ladder like Spiderman! But Mark Henry has something really bad in mind here!"

"Ooohh! Mark Henry with a World's Strongest Slam on top of the ladder! Kingston may be completely out of it!"

"Shelton Benjamin is looking for a head scissors here but MVP counters and delivers a huge powerbomb!"

"Now CM Punk and Christian are in a position to win the match, Christian with the Killswitch from the ladder! That looked brutal!"

"MVP was just tossed to the outside! He landed on Mark Henry and both of them appear to be out cold!"

"CM Punk and Kane have made their way up the ladder! This could end badly for both Superstars! Kane has his hand around Punk's throat! He may be looking for a Chokeslam!"

"Punk is desperately trying to fight Kane off! CM Punk just hit Kane with a huge martial arts kick that sent the big man crashing to the mat!"

"CM Punk has done it! CM Punk has won the Money in the Bank Ladder Match for the second year running! What an incredible performance from this amazing Superstar!"

WRESTLEMANIA VII

MARCH 24, 1991

Title: 'Superstars and Stripes Forever'
Location: Los Angeles, CA
Arena: Los Angeles Sports Arena
Attendance: 15,000

MATCH CARD

The Rockers def. Haku and The Barbarian w/ Bobby 'The Brain' Heenan

The Texas Tornado def. Dino Bravo

British Bulldog def. Warlord w/ Slick

World Tag Team Championship Match
The Nasty Boys w/ Jimmy Hart def. Hart Foundation to become new champions

Blindfold Match
Jake 'The Snake' Roberts def. 'The Model' Rick Martel

Undertaker w/ Paul Bearer def. 'Superfly' Jimmy Snuka

Retirement Match
Ultimate Warrior def. Randy 'Macho King' Savage w/ Queen Sherri

Genichiro Tenryu and Koji Kitao def. Demolition

Intercontinental Championship Match
Big Boss Man def. Mr. Perfect w/ Bobby 'The Brain' Heenan by DQ

Earthquake def. Greg 'The Hammer' Valentine

Legion of Doom def. Power and Glory (Hercules and Paul Roma), w/ Slick

Virgil w/ 'Rowdy' Roddy Piper def. 'Million Dollar Man' Ted DiBiase by count-out

The Mountie w/ Jimmy Hart def. Tito Santana

WWE Championship Match
Hulk Hogan def. Sgt. Slaughter w/ General Adnan to become new champion

DID YOU KNOW...

Shawn Michaels' match opened *WrestleMania VII* - he would also open VIII & IX.

WrestleMania VII was the final *WrestleMania* for Andre the Giant.

WrestleMania VII was planned for the LA Coliseum, it moved for security related to the Gulf War.

WRESTLEMANIA VIII

MATCH CARD

Shawn Michaels w/ Sensational Sherri def. 'El Matador' Tito Santana

Undertaker w/ Paul Bearer def. Jake 'The Snake' Roberts

Intercontinental Championship Match
Bret 'Hit Man' Hart def. 'Rowdy' Roddy Piper to become new champion

Hacksaw Jim Duggan, Sgt. Slaughter, Virgil and Big Boss Man def.
The Mountie, Repo Man and The Nasty Boys w/ Jimmy Hart

First Main Event - WWE Championship Match
Randy 'Macho Man' Savage w/ Elizabeth def. Ric Flair w/ Mr. Perfect to become new champion

Tatanka def. 'The Model' Rick Martel

World Tag Team Championship Match
Natural Disasters def. Money Inc. w/ Jimmy Hart by count-out

Owen Hart def. Skinner

Second Main Event
Hulk Hogan def. Sid Justice w/ Harvey Wippleman by DQ

DID YOU KNOW...

Legendary Ric Flair made his first *WrestleMania* appearance.

Ultimate Warrior made his return to World Wrestling Entertainment at *WrestleMania VIII*.

Jake 'The Snake' Roberts exited WWE after his loss to Undertaker at *WrestleMania VIII*

No 19

KING KONG BUNDY™

Statistics...

Name:
King Kong Bundy

Height:
6-foot-5

Weight:
450 pounds

From:
Atlantic City, NJ

Signature Move:
Bundy Splash

WrestleMania Record

March 31, 1985 – *WrestleMania*: King Kong Bundy (managed by Jimmy Hart) def. S.D. Jones at Madison Square Garden in a record nine seconds.

April 7, 1986 – *WrestleMania 2*: Hulk Hogan def. King Kong Bundy to retain the WWE Championship in a Steel Cage.

March 29, 1987 – *WrestleMania III*: King Kong Bundy shocked the world by giving his patented 'Bundy Splash' to Little Beaver in a Mixed Tag Match.

April 2, 1995 – *WrestleMania XI*: Undertaker def. King Kong Bundy w/Ted DiBiase.

'SUPERFLY' JIMMY SNUKA™

No 18

WrestleMania Record

March 31, 1985 – *WrestleMania*: 'Superfly' Jimmy Snuka was the guest corner man for Hulk Hogan and Mr. T.

April 2, 1989 – *WrestleMania V*: 'Superfly' Jimmy Snuka finally made his long awaited return to WWE.

April 1, 1990 – *WrestleMania VI*: Rick Rude def. 'Superfly' Jimmy Snuka.

March 24, 1991 – *WrestleMania VII*: 'Superfly' Jimmy Snuka was the first ever *WrestleMania* opponent for Undertaker.

April 5, 2009 – *WrestleMania XXV*: Chris Jericho def. Legends (Jimmy Snuka, Ricky Steamboat and Roddy Piper w/Ric Flair).

Statistics...

Name:
'Superfly' Jimmy Snuka

Height:
5-foot-10

Weight:
250 pounds

From:
Fiji

Signature Move:
Superfly Splash

THE BIG WRESTLEMANIA QUIZ PART IV

Round four of the *WrestleMania* Quiz is here! Do you have what it takes?

Q31. Where did *WrestleMania X* take place?

A. New York ☐
B. San Francisco ☐
C. Miami ☐

Q32. Who defeated Yokozuna for the WWE Championship at *WrestleMania X?*

A. Bret 'Hit Man' Hart ☐
B. Hulk Hogan ☐
C. Lex Luger ☐

Q34. Who did Lex Luger team with at *WrestleMania XI?*

A. British Bulldog ☐
B. Diesel ☐
C. Shawn Michaels ☐

Q33. Who is this Superstar that took part in a legendary Ladder Match at *WrestleMania X?*

A. Shawn Michaels ☐
B. Triple H ☐
C. Edge ☐

Q35. Who did Undertaker defeat at *WrestleMania XI?*

A. Jake 'The Snake' Roberts ☐
B. King Kong Bundy ☐
C. Kane ☐

Q36. Who did Bret 'Hit Man' Hart defeat in an 'I quit' match at *WrestleMania XI?*

A. Bob Backlund ☐
B. Pedro Morales ☐
C. Bruno Sammartino ☐

Q37. Which of these Superstars did not appear at *WrestleMania XII?*

A. The Nacho Man ☐
B. The Huckster ☐
C. Gillberg ☐

Q38. Who faced Stone Cold Steve Austin at *WrestleMania XII?*

A. Savio Vega ☐
B. Mideon ☐
C. Goldust ☐

Q39. What kind of match was contested for the WWE Championship at *WrestleMania XII?*

A. Ladder Match ☐
B. Iron Man Match ☐
C. Steel Cage Match ☐

Q40. Who is this Superstar that scored a shocking victory over Hunter Hearst Helmsley at *WrestleMania XII?*

A. Ultimate Warrior ☐
B. Renegade ☐
C. Ricky Morton ☐

JACK SWAGGER™

Height: **6-foot-4**
Weight: **263 pounds**
From: **Perry, OK**
Signature Move: **Gutwrench Powerbomb**

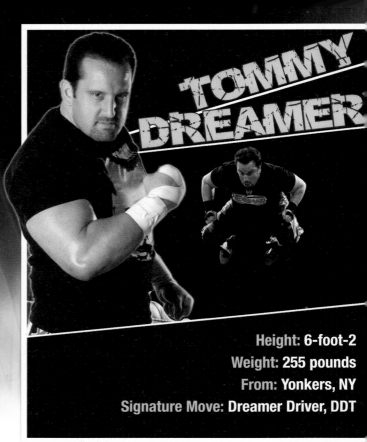

TOMMY DREAMER

Height: **6-foot-2**
Weight: **255 pounds**
From: **Yonkers, NY**
Signature Move: **Dreamer Driver, DDT**

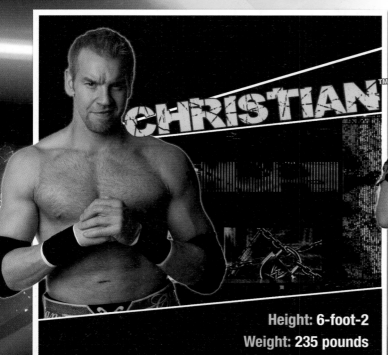

CHRISTIAN™

Height: **6-foot-2**
Weight: **235 pounds**
From: **Toronto, ON**
Signature Move: **Killswitch**

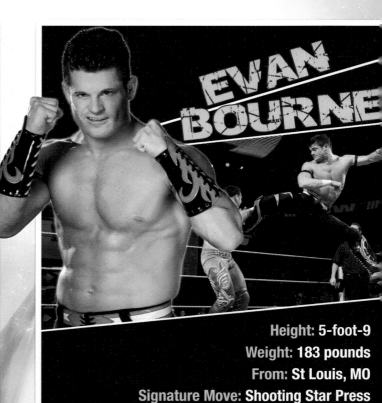

EVAN BOURNE

Height: **5-foot-9**
Weight: **183 pounds**
From: **St Louis, MO**
Signature Move: **Shooting Star Press**

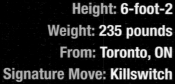

PAUL BURCHILL

Height: 6-foot-4
Weight: 247 pounds
From: Chelsea, England
Signature Move: Reverse Swinging Neckbreaker

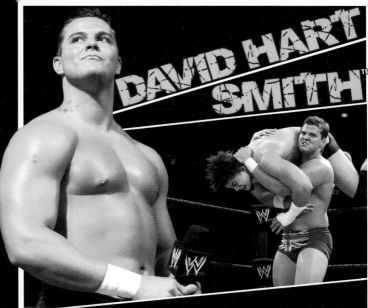

DAVID HART SMITH

Height: 6-foot-5
Weight: 260 pounds
From: Calgary, AB
Signature Move: Running Powerslam

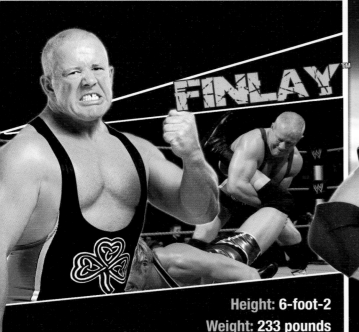

FINLAY

Height: 6-foot-2
Weight: 233 pounds
From: Belfast, Northern Ireland
Signature Move: The Celtic Cross

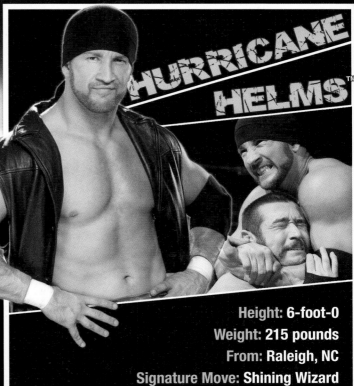

HURRICANE HELMS

Height: 6-foot-0
Weight: 215 pounds
From: Raleigh, NC
Signature Move: Shining Wizard

PROFILES

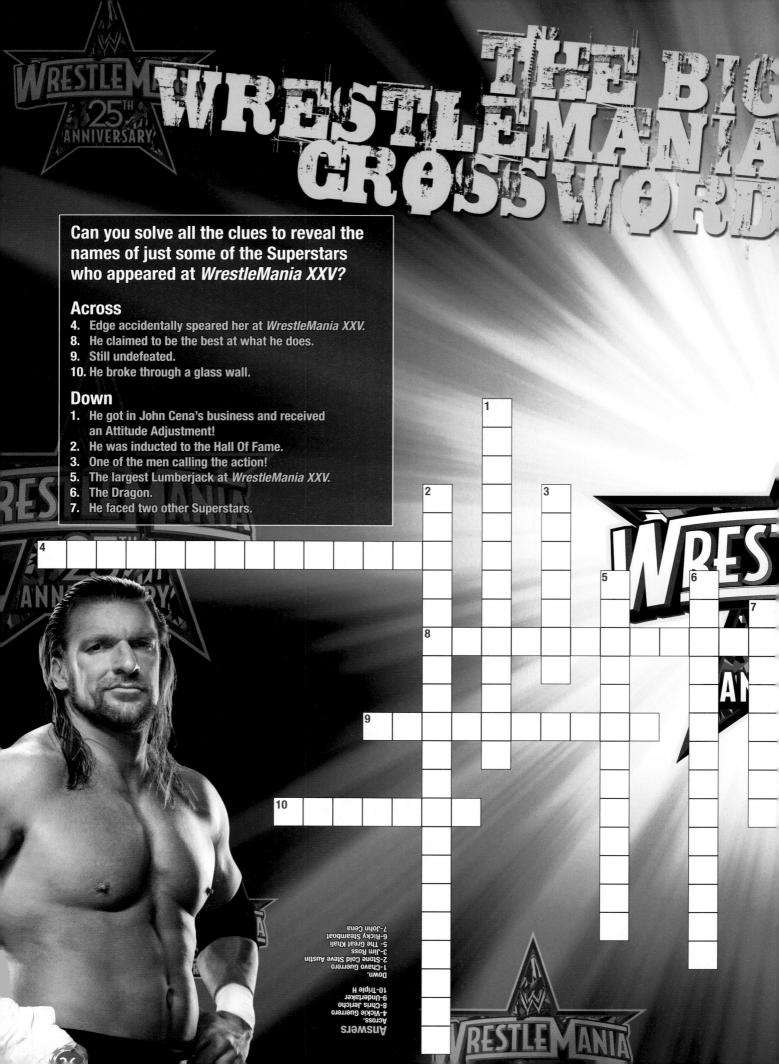

THE BIG WRESTLEMANIA CROSSWORD

Can you solve all the clues to reveal the names of just some of the Superstars who appeared at *WrestleMania XXV*?

Across
4. Edge accidentally speared her at *WrestleMania XXV*.
8. He claimed to be the best at what he does.
9. Still undefeated.
10. He broke through a glass wall.

Down
1. He got in John Cena's business and received an Attitude Adjustment!
2. He was inducted to the Hall Of Fame.
3. One of the men calling the action!
5. The largest Lumberjack at *WrestleMania XXV*.
6. The Dragon.
7. He faced two other Superstars.

Answers
Across.
4-Vickie Guerrero
8-Chris Jericho
9-Underetaker
10-Triple H

Down.
1-Chavo Guerrero
2-Stone Cold Steve Austin
3-Jim Ross
5- The Great Khali
6-Ricky Steamboat
7-John Cena

THE BIG WRESTLEMANIA WORD SEARCH

Can you find all ten Superstars hiding in this word search?

M	Y	N	G	K	I	T	J	V	U	I	F	Z	M	A
R	D	X	W	K	W	A	X	C	H	F	Y	I	S	L
A	R	H	R	W	N	M	W	A	D	G	V	H	O	J
N	A	U	B	R	A	E	W	R	N	U	D	T	E	J
D	H	W	D	D	C	B	O	L	F	J	E	W	P	I
Y	F	S	H	A	W	N	M	I	C	H	A	E	L	S
O	F	Y	D	R	A	H	T	T	A	M	D	N	F	B
R	E	P	I	P	Y	D	D	O	R	Y	D	W	O	R
T	J	L	L	H	R	F	M	F	Y	T	F	M	A	C
O	S	E	K	R	A	P	S	D	R	A	H	C	I	R
N	R	I	C	F	L	A	I	R	P	E	M	E	H	O
B	I	G	S	H	O	W	N	X	W	S	N	P	R	U
A	N	E	C	N	H	O	J	X	T	O	I	Z	Y	C
S	A	N	T	I	N	A	M	A	R	E	L	L	A	R
H	C	X	C	D	U	H	M	I	F	H	B	F	W	O

BIG SHOW ☐	RANDY ORTON ☐
CARLITO ☐	RIC FLAIR ☐
JEFF HARDY ☐	ROWDY RODDY PIPER ☐
JOHN CENA ☐	SANTINA MARELLA ☐
MATT HARDY ☐	SHAWN MICHAELS ☐

For answers look on page 41.

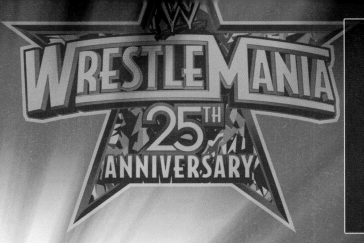

For answers look on page 41.

At *WrestleMania XXV,* the undefeated Undertaker took on Mr WrestleMania himself, Shawn Michaels. As the bell tolled, Undertaker was revealed as the last man standing. Check out the action from the match in the picture, shown left. Add some colour to proceedings with your crayons or felt tip pens.

Page 37 Word Search Answers...

M	Y	N	G	K	I	T	J	V	U	I	F	Z	M	A
R	D	X	W	K	W	A	X	C	H	F	Y	I	S	L
A	R	H	R	W	N	M	W	A	D	G	V	H	O	J
N	A	U	B	R	A	E	W	R	N	U	D	T	E	J
D	H	W	D	D	C	B	O	L	F	J	E	W	P	I
Y	F	S	H	A	W	N	M	I	C	H	A	E	L	S
O	F	Y	D	R	A	H	T	T	A	M	D	N	F	B
R	E	P	I	P	Y	D	D	O	R	Y	D	W	O	R
T	J	L	L	H	R	F	M	F	Y	T	F	M	A	C
O	S	E	K	R	A	P	S	D	R	A	H	C	I	R
N	R	I	C	F	L	A	I	R	P	E	M	E	H	O
B	I	G	S	H	O	W	N	X	W	S	N	P	R	U
A	N	E	C	N	H	O	J	X	T	O	I	Z	Y	C
S	A	N	T	I	N	A	M	A	R	E	L	L	A	R
H	C	X	C	D	U	H	M	I	F	H	B	F	W	O

Page 38 Spot The Difference Answers...

Page 39 Spot The Difference Answers...

WRESTLEMANIA IX

APRIL 4, 1993

MATCH CARD

Intercontinental Championship Match
Tatanka def. Shawn Michaels w/ Luna Vachon by count-out

The Steiner Brothers def. The Headshrinkers w/ Afa

Doink def. Crush

Razor Ramon def. Bob Backlund

World Tag Team Championship Match
Money Inc. def. Hulk Hogan and Brutus 'The Barber' Beefcake w/ Jimmy Hart by DQ

'The Narcissist' Lex Luger def. Mr. Perfect

Undertaker w/ Paul Bearer def. Giant Gonzales w/ Harvey Wippleman by DQ

WWE Championship Match
Yokozuna w/ Mr. Fuji and Jim Cornette def. Bret 'Hit Man' Hart to become new champion

After the match, Hulk Hogan def. Yokozuna w/ Mr. Fuji and Jim Cornette to become new champion

DID YOU KNOW...

The WWE Championship changed hands twice at *WrestleMania IX*. First, Yokozuna defeated Bret Hart and, moments later, Hulk Hogan defeated Yokozuna.

WrestleMania IX was the first *WrestleMania* event held entirely outdoors.

WWF WrestleMania X

MARCH 20, 1994

MATCH CARD

Owen Hart def. Bret 'Hit Man' Hart

Mixed Tag Match
Bam Bam Bigelow and Luna Vachon def. Doink and Dink

Falls Count Anywhere Match
Randy 'Macho Man' Savage def. Crush w/ Mr. Fuji

Women's Championship Match
Alundra Blayze def. Leilani Kai to retain

WWE Championship Match
Yokozuna w/ Mr. Fuji and Jim Cornette def. Lex Luger by DQ (Mr. Perfect was special guest referee)

Ladder Match for the Intercontinental Championship
Razor Ramon def. Shawn Michaels to retain

World Tag Team Championship Match
Men on a Mission w/ Oscar def. The Quebecers w/ Johnny Polo by count-out

Earthquake def. Adam Bomb w/ Harvey Wippleman

WWE Championship Match
Bret 'Hit Man' Hart def. Yokozuna w/ Mr. Fuji and Jim Cornette to become new champion

DID YOU KNOW...

WrestleMania X was the first *WrestleMania* not to feature Hulk Hogan.

Tickets sold out so quickly for *WrestleMania X* at Madison Square Garden that the show was also shown at the adjacent Paramount Theatre on closed-circuit television.

No 17

MR PERFECT™

Statistics...

Name:
Mr Perfect

Height:
6-foot-3

Weight:
260 pounds

From:
Robbinsdale, MN

Signature Move:
Perfect-Plex

WrestleMania Record

April 2, 1989 – WrestleMania V: Mr Perfect def. the Blue Blazer.

April 1, 1990 – WrestleMania VI: Brutus 'The Barber' Beefcake def. Mr Perfect.

March 24, 1991 – WrestleMania VII: Big Bossman def. Mr Perfect.

April 4, 1993 – WrestleMania IX: Lex Luger def. Mr Perfect.

March 20, 1994 – WrestleMania X: Mr. Perfect refereed a match between Lex Luger and Yokozuna, DQ'ing Luger in the process.

April 1, 2007 – WrestleMania 23: The Hennig Family (representing Mr Perfect) was introduced to the audience at Ford Field, as Mr Perfect was honoured among the WWE Hall of Fame Class of 2007.

'ROWDY' RODDY PIPER™

No 16

WrestleMania Record

March 31, 1985 – WrestleMania: Hulk Hogan & Mr. T def. 'Rowdy' Roddy Piper & Paul Orndorff.

April 7, 1986 – WrestleMania 2: Disqualified vs Mr T in a Boxing Match.

March 29, 1987 – WrestleMania III: Defeated Adrian Adonis.

April 2, 1989 – WrestleMania V: Hosted Piper's Pit interviewing WWE Stars

April 1, 1990 – WrestleMania VI: 'Rowdy' Roddy Piper & 'Bad News' Brown ended in a double count-out.

April 5, 1992 – WrestleMania VIII: Bret 'Hit Man' Hart defeated 'Rowdy' Roddy Piper.

March 20, 1994 – WrestleMania X: Refereed a Match between Bret 'Hit Man' Hart and Yokozuna.

March 31, 1996 – WrestleMania XII: Defeated Goldust.

March 30, 2003 – WrestleMania XIX: 'Rowdy' Roddy Piper whacked Hulk Hogan with a steel pipe!

April 3, 2005 – WrestleMania 21: Hosted Piper's Pit.

April 5, 2009 – WrestleMania XXV: Chris Jericho defeated Legends including Roddy Piper.

Statistics...

Name:
'Rowdy' Roddy Piper

Height:
6-foot-2

Weight:
230 pounds

From:
Glasgow, Scotland

Signature Move:
Sleeper Hold

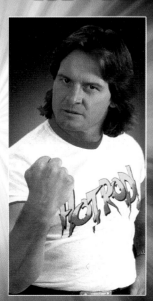

THE BIG WRESTLEMANIA QUIZ PART V

Let's get going with Round 5 of the *WrestleMania* Quiz! Do you have what it takes?

Q41. Who faced The Sultan at *WrestleMania 13*?

A. The Rock ☐

B. Stone Cold Steve Austin ☐

C. Triple H ☐

Q42. Who teamed with British Bulldog at *WrestleMania 13*?

A. Owen Hart ☐

B. Bret 'Hit Man' Hart ☐

C. Undertaker ☐

Q43. Who won the opening bout at *WrestleMania XIV*?

A. The Headshrinkers ☐

B. LOD 2000 ☐

C. Money Inc. ☐

Q44. Who is this Superstar that Undertaker defeated at *WrestleMania 13*?

A. Giant Gonzales ☐

B. Sycho Sid ☐

C. King Kong Bundy ☐

Q45. Who was the special enforcer for the main event at *WrestleMania XIV*?

A. Butterbean ☐

B. Mr McMahon ☐

C. Mike Tyson ☐

Q46. Who did Goldust team with in his mixed tag team match at *WrestleMania XIV*?

A. Terri ☐

B. Luna Vachon ☐

C. Trish Stratus ☐

Q47. Who faced Triple H at *WrestleMania XV*?

A. Kane ☐

B. Big Show ☐

C. Undertaker ☐

Q48. Who won the WWE Championship at *WrestleMania XV*?

A. The Rock ☐

B. Triple H ☐

C. Stone Cold Steve Austin ☐

Q49. Where did *WrestleMania XV* take place?

A. New York ☐

B. Philadelphia ☐

C. Chicago ☐

Q50. Who is this Superstar that retained the European Championship at *WrestleMania XV*?

A. Mr McMahon ☐

B. Shane McMahon ☐

C. Randy Orton ☐

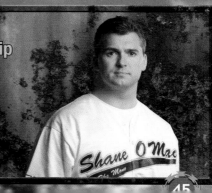

45

KOKO B WARE™

Height: **5-foot-8**
Weight: **240 pounds**
From: **Union City, TN**
Signature Move: **Bird Buster**

GORILLA MONSOON

Height: **6-foot-5**
Weight: **400 pounds**
From: **Manchuria, NY**
Signature Move: **Airplane Spin, Manchurian Splash**

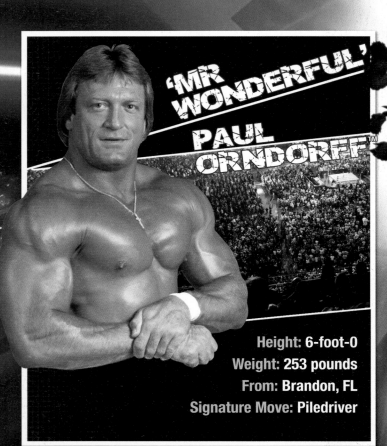

'MR WONDERFUL' PAUL ORNDORFF™

Height: **6-foot-0**
Weight: **253 pounds**
From: **Brandon, FL**
Signature Move: **Piledriver**

CHIEF JAY STRONGBOW

Height: **6-foot-0**
Weight: **265 pounds**
From: **Pawhuska, OK**
Signature Move: **Tomahawk Chop, Sleeper Hold**

HALL OF FAME

Each year, just before *WrestleMania*, WWE honours the Superstars of the past who have made WWE what it is today with a special ceremony for

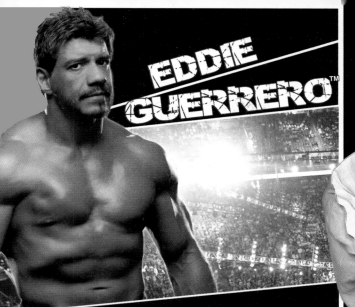

EDDIE GUERRERO™

Height: **5-foot-8**
Weight: **220 pounds**
From: **El Paso, TX**
Signature Move: **Frog Splash**

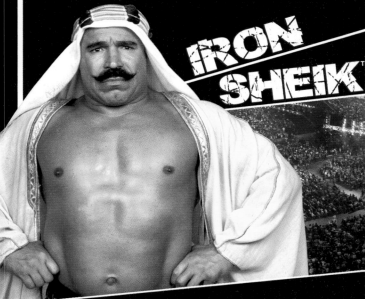

IRON SHEIK™

Height: **6-foot-0**
Weight: **258 pounds**
From: **Tehran, Iran**
Signature Move: **Camel Clutch**

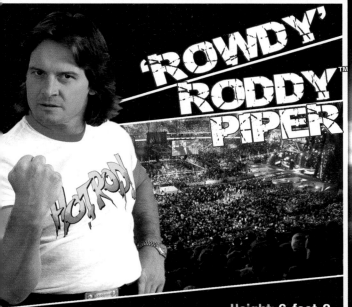

'ROWDY' RODDY PIPER™

Height: **6-foot-2**
Weight: **220 pounds**
From: **Scotland**
Signature Move: **Sleephold**

JUNKYARD DOG™

Height: **6-foot-3**
Weight: **280 pounds**
From: **Charlotte, NC**
Signature Move: **'Thump' Powerslam**

the WWE Hall Of Fame inductees.
Here are a few of the legendary
performers who have been inducted
over the years.

PROFILES

47

HANDICAP MATCH:
CHRIS JERICHO VS ROWDY RODDY PIPER, JIMMY "SUPERFLY" SNUKA, & RICKY "THE DRAGON" STEAMBOAT WITH "NATURE BOY" RIC FLAIR IN THEIR CORNER

"Making his way to the ring is Chris Jericho. The odds may appear to be stacked against him but we cannot underestimate this young Superstar."

"And here are the team of WWE Legends accompanied by the one and only, Ric Flair!"

"It will be 'Rowdy' Roddy Piper to start things off and he immediately takes Jericho down!"

"Piper just hit Jericho with a dropkick! I don't think I have seen 'Rowdy' Roddy Piper hit a dropkick since WrestleMania 1!"

"Piper makes the tag to 'Superfly' Jimmy Snuka! And just listen to the reaction from the crowd!"

"'Superfly' Jimmy Snuka with a series of left and right hands to the gut of Chris Jericho! The Legends are looking great tonight!"

"Snuka makes the tag and here comes Ricky 'The Dragon' Steamboat. Steamboat looks to be in great shape as he sails from the top rope to deliver a huge chop!"

"I don't think that Jericho was expecting the Legends to put up such a fight in the early going."

"Steamboat with a classic armdrag! That takes me back to the late 80s when Steamboat and Flair used to tear up the ring in the old NWA!"

"Both Ricky Steamboat and 'Superfly' Jimmy Snuka are in the ring and hit Jericho with a double chop to the chest! No one does it quite like these two Legends!"

"But look at this! Jericho has 'Superfly' Jimmy Snuka locked into the Walls of Jericho! And Snuka is forced to tap out!"

"'Rowdy' Roddy Piper is back in the ring and delivers a boot to Jericho's gut. His offence may well be bowling shoe ugly, but it sure is effective!"

"Out of nowhere, Jericho hits Piper with the ensuguri! Piper is down and out! 1…2…3! Jericho just pinned Piper! Things are really looking up for Y2J!"

"Jericho hasn't seen Steamboat climb to the top! Steamboat with the flying crossbody!"

"Ricky 'The Dragon' Steamboat came so close to pinning Jericho there, but Y2J is back in control!"

"Jericho with another devastating clothesline! Ricky 'The Dragon' Steamboat is in trouble here!"

"Ric Flair is up on the apron, and Jericho just hit him with a cheap shot!"

"But look at this, the distraction by Flair has given Ricky 'The Dragon' Steamboat time to recover! And he just dumped Jericho over the top rope!"

"Ricky 'The Dragon' Steamboat is going high risk here!"

"Ricky 'The Dragon' Steamboat just dove over the top rope and landed on Jericho! What an incredible move from this WWE Legend!"

"Jericho was looking woozy there for a moment but he has come back with a huge bulldog that drives Ricky 'The Dragon' Steamboat's face into the canvas!"

"Steamboat has gone back to the top rope to deliver yet another chop to the head of Chris Jericho!"

"Jericho went for the Lionsault but Ricky 'The Dragon' Steamboat somehow managed to roll out of the way! This match is incredible!"

"Ricky 'The Dragon' Steamboat with a huge powerslam!"

"Jericho has countered and has Ricky 'The Dragon' Steamboat in the Walls Of Jericho! Steamboat may have to tap out just like 'Superfly' Jimmy Snuka did earlier in the match!"

"Ricky 'The Dragon' Steamboat made it to the ropes but Jericho is looking for the Codebreaker here!"

"Jericho hits the Codebreaker! This match may well be over!"

"Jericho is going for the pin! 1…2…3! Jericho has done it! Jericho has won the match!"

"Here comes Ric Flair! Flair has Jericho in the corner and delivers a series of chops!"

"Jericho has broken away! And look at this! Another Codebreaker!"

"Codebreaker to Flair!"

"The Legends put up an incredible fight but at the end of the match it is Chris Jericho who has had his hand raised! What a match!"

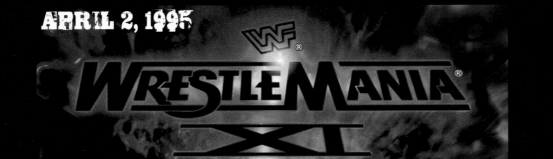

MATCH CARD

Lex Luger and British Bulldog def. Eli and Jacob Blu w/ Uncle Zebekiah

Intercontinental Championship Match
Razor Ramon w/ 1-2-3 Kid def. Jeff Jarrett w/ The Roadie by DQ

Undertaker w/ Paul Bearer def. King Kong Bundy w/ 'Million Dollar Man' Ted DiBiase

World Tag Team Championship Match
Owen Hart and Yokozuna w/ Mr. Fuji and Jim Cornette def. Smoking Gunns to become new champions

"I Quit" Match
Bret 'Hit Man' Hart def. Bob Backlund

WWE Championship Match
Diesel def. Shawn Michaels to retain

Lawrence Taylor w/ Ken Norton, Jr, Carl Banks, Rickey Jackson, Steve McMichael, Chris Spielman and Reggie White def. Bam Bam Bigelow w/ Million Dollar Corporation

DID YOU KNOW...

WrestleMania XI aired just one month before the first-ever '*In Your House*' pay-per-view event.

WrestleMania XI was the one and only held in Connecticut – home of WWE corporate headquarters.

Pamela Anderson accompanied Diesel to the ring for his match.

MARCH 31, 1996

MATCH CARD

Owen Hart, British Bulldog and Vader w/ Jim Cornette def.
Yokozuna, Jake 'The Snake' Roberts and Ahmed Johnson

Hollywood Backlot Brawl
'Rowdy' Roddy Piper def. Goldust w/ Marlena

The Ringmaster w/ 'Million Dollar Man' Ted DiBiase def. Savio Vega

Ultimate Warrior def. Hunter Hearst Helmsley w/ Sable

Undertaker w/ Paul Bearer def. Diesel

Iron Man Match for the WWE Championship
Shawn Michaels def. Bret 'Hit Man' Hart in overtime to become new champion

DID YOU KNOW...

Stone Cold and Triple H both made their *WrestleMania* debuts at *WrestleMania XII*.

WrestleMania XII featured just six matches, and for good reason - the main event was a 60-minute Iron Man Match between Bret Hart and Shawn Michaels.

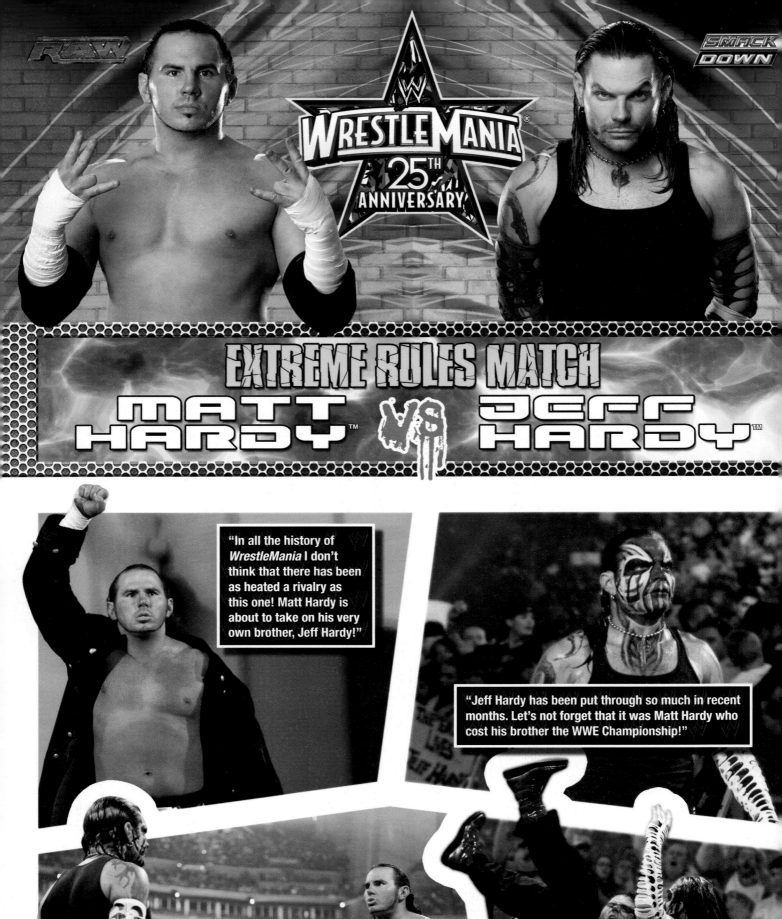

RAW

SMACK DOWN

WRESTLEMANIA 25TH ANNIVERSARY

EXTREME RULES MATCH
MATT HARDY™ VS JEFF HARDY™

"In all the history of *WrestleMania* I don't think that there has been as heated a rivalry as this one! Matt Hardy is about to take on his very own brother, Jeff Hardy!"

"Jeff Hardy has been put through so much in recent months. Let's not forget that it was Matt Hardy who cost his brother the WWE Championship!"

"What must Jeff and Matt's father be thinking sat at home watching his sons go at it?"

"And the match is underway, Jeff Hardy takes it straight to the outside and knocks his brother into the barrier!"

"Jeff Hardy is looking to finish the match quickly with a Whisper in the Wind, but Matt counters with a vicious chair shot!"

"Just look at Matt Hardy go to town on his brother with that steel chair!"

"Matt Hardy has his brother tied up in the ropes and is just wrenching back on his neck!"

"Matt Hardy continues to pound away on his brother! Matt is relentless tonight!"

"And what was that? Matt Hardy just found a vacuum cleaner under the ring and nailed Jeff in the face with it!"

"Jeff Hardy is whipped into the corner by his brother but manages to counter the big splash attempt!"

"I thought Jeff Hardy was getting back into the match for a moment but from out of nowhere, Matt Hardy hits the Side Effect!"

"I'm not sure how much more of this Jeff can take, the body is not meant to bend like that!"

"Matt Hardy has his brother down in the corner and is really laying the boots in!"

"Look at this! Jeff Hardy has somehow mustered the energy to hit Matt with a flying clothesline on the outside!"

"Matt Hardy's head just bounced off the ring steps!"

"Jeff Hardy has a trashcan, what is he going to do here?"

"Matt Hardy is down and out in the corner... Mule Kick to the face through the trashcan! What an incredible move!"

"Jeff Hardy is in control of the match as he drives Matt face first into the canvas!"

"Jeff Hardy is going for the Swanton Bomb! But Matt rolls out of the way!"

"Jeff is running on pure adrenaline here as he takes his brother to the top rope and delivers a superplex!"

"Jeff Hardy has his brother sandwiched between two tables! What is he thinking! This could end both of their careers!"

"Jeff Hardy just delivered a huge Swanton Bomb to his brother putting him through not one but two tables!"

"Jeff Hardy has now set up two ladders in the ring! Where do all these ladders come from?"

"Jeff Hardy is going for a leg drop from the top of that twenty foot ladder!"

"Somehow Matt Hardy managed to roll out of the way and avoid being crushed by his younger sibling!"

"Jeff Hardy may have just broken his back! He landed spine first from a good twenty five feet up!"

"Matt Hardy can take the advantage here! What is he doing? He has wrapped a chair around Jeff Hardy's neck!"

"Twist of Fate on the steel chair! Matt Hardy may have ended his brother's career right there!"

"Matt Hardy gets the pin and the victory! We need to get some help out here for Jeff! He looks seriously injured!"

No 15 — THE HARDY BOYZ™

Statistics...

Name: **Matt Hardy**
Height: **6-foot-2**
Weight: **236 pounds**
From: **Cameron, NC**
Signature Move:
Twist of Fate

Name: **Jeff Hardy**
Height: **6-foot-1**
Weight: **225 pounds**
From: **Cameron, NC**
Signature Move:
**Swanton Bomb,
Whisper in the Wind**

WrestleMania Record

April 2, 2000 – *WrestleMania 2000:* Edge & Christian defeated The Hardy Boyz and The Dudley Boyz in a 3-Way Ladder match.

April 1, 2001 – *WrestleMania X-7:* Edge & Christian defeated The Dudley Boyz and The Hardy Boyz.

March 17, 2002 – *WrestleMania X8:* Billy & Chuck defeated The Hardy Boyz, Dudley Boyz and APA to retain their Tag Championship.

March 30, 2003 – *WrestleMania 19:* Matt Hardy defeated Rey Mysterio to retain the Cruiserweight Championship.

April 2, 2006 – *WrestleMania 22:* RVD beat Matt Hardy & others in a Money in the Bank Ladder Match.

April 1, 2007 – *WrestleMania 23:* Mr. Kennedy beat Jeff Hardy & others in a Money In The Bank Ladder Match.

March 30, 2008 – *WrestleMania XXIV:* Matt Hardy unannounced spoilt MVP's chances of winning the Money in the Bank Ladder Match.

April 5, 2009 – *WrestleMania 25:* Matt Hardy defeated Jeff Hardy in a brother-vs-brother Extreme Rules match!

Sgt. SLAUGHTER™ — No 14

WrestleMania Record

March 24, 1991 – *WrestleMania VII:* Hulk Hogan def. Sgt. Slaughter for the WWE Championship.

April 5, 1992 – *WrestleMania VIII:* Hacksaw Jim Duggan, Sgt. Slaughter, Virgil and Big Bossman def. The Mountie, Repo Man and The Nasty Boys.

March 14, 2004 – *WrestleMania XX:* Sgt. Slaughter was honoured with all the other Hall of Fame inductees during the pay-per-view.

April 1, 2007 – *WrestleMania 23:* Sgt. Slaughter made a brief cameo during a backstage dance party started by Cryme Tyme.

Statistics...

Name:
Sgt. Slaughter

Height:
6-foot-4

Weight:
300 pounds

From:
Parris Island, SC

Signature Move:
Cobra Clutch

No 13   RANDY 'MACHO MAN' SAVAGE™

Statistics...

Name:
Randy 'Macho Man' Savage

Height:
6-foot-2

Weight:
273 pounds

From:
Sarasota, FL

Signature Move:
Flying Elbow Drop

WrestleMania Record

April 7, 1986 – *WrestleMania 2*: Successfully defended the Intercontinental Championship against George 'The Animal' Steel.

March 29, 1987 – *WrestleMania III*: Def. by Ricky Steamboat in perhaps the greatest match in WWE history.

March 27, 1988 – *WrestleMania IV*: Won a 14-Man Tournament to be crowned the WWE Champion!

April 5, 1989 – *WrestleMania V*: 'The Mega Powers Explode': Hulk Hogan def. Randy 'Macho Man' Savage to win the WWE Championship

April 1, 1990 *WrestleMania VI*: Macho King and Queen Sherri were def. by Dusty Rhodes and Sapphire.

March 24, 1991 - *WrestleMania VII*: Ultimate Warrior def. the Macho King in a 'Retirement Match' forcing Randy into retirement.

April 5, 1992 - *WrestleMania VIII*: Def. Ric Flair to become WWE Champion for the second time in his career!

March 20, 1994 - *WrestleMania X*: Def. Crush in a 'Falls Count Anywhere Match'.

JOHN CENA®   No 12

WrestleMania Record

March 14, 2004 – *WrestleMania XX*: John Cena defeats Big Show to win the U.S. Title.

April 3, 2005 – *WrestleMania 21*: John Cena defeats JBL to win WWE Championship.

April 2, 2006 – *WrestleMania 22*: John Cena defeats Triple H.

April 1, 2007 – *WrestleMania 23*: John Cena defeats Shawn Michaels.

March 30, 2008 – *WrestleMania XXIV*: Randy Orton defeats Triple H and John Cena.

April 5, 2009 – *WrestleMania 25*: John Cena defeats World Heavyweight Champion Edge and Big Show to win the title.

Statistics...

Name:
John Cena

Height:
6-foot-1

Weight:
240 pounds

From:
West Newbury, MA

Signature Move:
Attitude Adjustment, STF

13 WRESTLEMANIA HEAT!

MARCH 23, 1997

MATCH CARD

No. 1 Contenders Tag Team Fatal Four Way Elimination Match
The Headbangers def. The Godwinns w/ Hillbilly Jim, The New Blackjacks and Doug Furnas and Phil LaFon

Intercontinental Championship Match
Rocky Maivia def. The Sultan w/ Bob Backlund and Iron Sheik to retain

Hunter Hearst Helmsley w/ Chyna def. Goldust w/ Marlena

World Tag Team Championship Match
Owen Hart and British Bulldog vs Mankind and Vader w/ Paul Bearer went to a double count-out

Submission Match
Bret 'Hit Man' Hart def. Stone Cold Steve Austin (Ken Shamrock was special guest referee)

Chicago Street Fight
Ahmed Johnson and Legion of Doom def. Nation of Domination

WWE Championship Match
Undertaker def. Sycho Sid to become the new WWE Champion

DID YOU KNOW...

WrestleMania 13 took place in the same arena as *WrestleMania 2*.

Bret Hart and Steve Austin later confessed that their match at *WrestleMania 13* was their favourite.

At this event, Bret Hart competed in his 12th consecutive *WrestleMania*.

MARCH 29, 1998

MATCH CARD

Tag Team Battle Royal

Legion of Doom w/ Sunny def. Savio Vega and Miquel Perez, Truth Commission, Bradshaw and Chainz, Mark Henry and D-Lo Brown, Quebecers, Rock N' Roll Express, Faarooq and Kama, Jose Estrada and Jesus Castillo, Headbangers, Scott Taylor and Brian Christopher, The D.O.A., The Godwinns and the New Midnight Express

Light Heavyweight Championship Match

Taka Michinoku def. Aguila to retain

European Championship Match

Triple H w/ Chyna def. Owen Hart to retain

Mixed Tag Team Match

Marc Mero and Sable def. The Artist Formerly Known as Goldust and Luna

Intercontinental Championship Match

The Rock w/ Nation of Domination def. Ken Shamrock after reverse decision when Shamrock would not release the ankle lock

Dumpster Match for World Tag Team Championship

Cactus Jack and Terry Funk def. New Age Outlaws to become new champions

Undertaker def. Kane w/ Paul Bearer

WWE Championship Match

Stone Cold Steve Austin def. Shawn Michaels w/ D-Generation X
(Mike Tyson was special ring enforcer)

DID YOU KNOW...

Pete Rose made his first *WrestleMania* appearance at *WrestleMania XIV*, where he was attacked by Kane.

Boxer Mike Tyson served as the special 'ringside enforcer' at *WrestleMania XIV* for the main event between Shawn Michaels and Stone Cold.

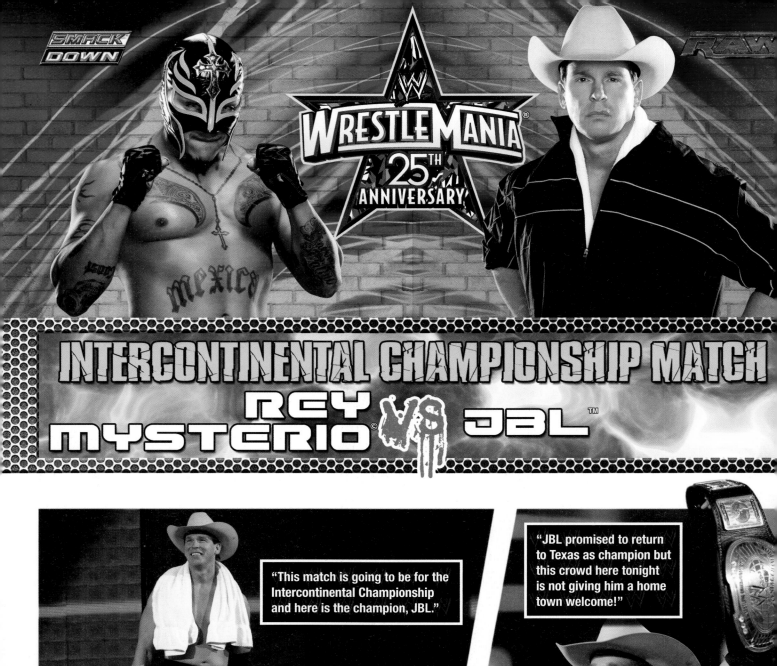

WRESTLEMANIA 25TH ANNIVERSARY

INTERCONTINENTAL CHAMPIONSHIP MATCH
REY MYSTERIO© VS JBL™

"This match is going to be for the Intercontinental Championship and here is the champion, JBL."

"JBL promised to return to Texas as champion but this crowd here tonight is not giving him a home town welcome!"

"JBL has to be the favourite in this match, he outweighs his opponent and certainly has the height advantage!"

"JBL has pretty much renounced his Texan heritage and now spends all his time in New York City!"

"And here is his opponent, the always exciting, Rey Mysterio!"

"Rey Mysterio is incredibly popular with our WWE fans!"

"Just look at all the kids in the crowd wearing their Rey Mysterio masks! It is pretty obvious who the crowd want to see win here tonight!"

"Mysterio enters the ring and look at that! JBL just booted Mysterio in the face before the bell has even rung! What a cheap shot!"

"JBL is hammering away at Mysterio! The referee hasn't even started the match yet!"

"The referee is checking on Rey Mysterio and asking him whether he wants to continue the match or not! This may be over even before it has officially begun!"

"The bell rings and the match is officially underway! JBL may have caused too much damage to Mysterio for him to even have a chance in this match!

"Don't count Rey Mysterio out just yet though! Rey comes back with a kick to the back of JBL's head!"

"And he follows it up with a drop kick that sends JBL into the ropes! He may be set up for the 619!"

"Here comes Rey Mysterio! 619!!! 619!!!"

"Rey Mysterio hits the 619 on JBL and the champion is reeling!"

"Mysterio has climbed to the top rope! He is going for the Frog Splash from the top!"

"If Mysterio hits this move the match could very well be over!"

"Mysterio is going for the pin! 1...2...3! Mysterio has won it! Mysterio is the Intercontinental Champion!"

"Rey cannot believe it! He has won the Intercontinental Championship for the first time in his career!"

"The underdog from San Diego, California has just created *WrestleMania* history!"

"Rey Mysterio reigns supreme here at *WrestleMania XXV!* Using a move inspired by his old friend Eddie Guerrero, Mysterio has defeated JBL in just 21 seconds!"

"Look at JBL, he can't believe what has just happened!"

"JBL is absolutely devastated! I think he may have underestimated his opponent here tonight!"

"I'm not sure that Rey Mysterio can believe it either! What an incredible *WrestleMania* moment!"

"JBL looks disgusted by the entire event! And the crowd here are showing him no sympathy at all!"

"Whenever you watch Rey Mysterio perform, you have to expect the unexpected!"

"And to win the match in just 21 seconds, that must be some kind of record!"

"Rey Mysterio has fought for everything he has ever achieved in his career and tonight he has been rewarded with the Intercontinental Championship!"

"JBL is very upset here! Oh my God! JBL just quit! JBL is leaving WWE!"

"JBL is such a sore loser! He is taking his ball and going home!"

No 11   ANDRE THE GIANT™

Statistics...

Name:
Andre The Giant

Height:
7-foot-4

Weight:
500 pounds

From:
Grenoble, France

Signature Move:
Sitdown Splash,
Double Underhook
Suplex

WrestleMania Record

March 31, 1985 – *WrestleMania:* Andre The Giant def. Big John Studd w/Bobby Heenan in a Body Slam Challenge.

April 5, 1986 – *WrestleMania II:* Andre The Giant won a 20-Man Invitational Battle Royal which included NFL players.

March 29, 1987 – *WrestleMania III:* Hulk Hogan def. Andre The Giant in front of the largest crowd ever for a WWE event.

March 27, 1988 – *WrestleMania IV:* Andre the Giant w/ Ted DiBiase & Virgil vs. Hulk Hogan went to a Double-DQ.

April 1, 1990 – *WrestleMania VI:* Demolition (Ax and Smash) def. Andre The Giant and Haku to win back the World Tag Team Championships.

THE ROCK®   No 10

WrestleMania Record

March 23, 1997 – *WrestleMania 13:* Rocky Maivia def. The Sultan w/Bob Backlund & Iron Sheik to retain the Intercontinental Championship.

March 29, 1998 – *WrestleMania XIV:* Rocky Maivia w/The Nation def. Ken Shamrock to retain the Intercontinental Championship.

March 28, 1999 – *WrestleMania XV:* Stone Cold Steve Austin def. The Rock in a No Holds Barred match to win the WWE Championship.

April 2, 2000 – *WrestleMania 2000:* Triple H def. The Rock, Mick Foley and Big Show in a Fatal Four Way match

April 1, 2001 – *WrestleMania X-7:* Stone Cold Steve Austin def. The Rock in a 'No DQ' match to win the WWE Championship, Mr McMahon helped Austin win.

March 17, 2002 – *WrestleMania X8:* Toronto Skydome: The Rock pins 'Hollywood' Hulk Hogan in an incredible spectacle of a match.

March 30, 2003 – *WrestleMania XIX:* The Rock def. Stone Cold Steve Austin after nailing three Rock Bottoms.

March 14, 2004 – *WrestleMania XX:* Randy Orton, Batista and Ric Flair beat Mick Foley and The Rock when Orton pinned Foley.

Statistics...

Name:
The Rock

Height:
6-foot-5

Weight:
260 pounds

From:
Miami, FL

Signature Move:
Rock Bottom;
People's Elbow

THE BIG WRESTLEMANIA QUIZ PART VI

More than half way through the *WrestleMania* quiz now! How do you think you are doing?

Q51. Who won the Hardcore Battle Royal at *WrestleMania 2000?*

A. Big Bossman ☐
B. Jeff Hardy ☐
C. Hardcore Holly ☐

Q52. Who won the Tag Team Championship in the first-ever TLC Match to be held at *WrestleMania 2000?*

A. Edge and Christian ☐
B. The Hardys ☐
C. The Dudley Boyz ☐

Q53. Who pinned Eddie Guerrero at *WrestleMania 2000?*

A. Chyna ☐
B. Edge ☐
C. Rey Mysterio ☐

Q54. Who is this Superstar that attempted to capture the Intercontinental Championship at *WrestleMania X-7?*

A. Chris Jericho ☐
B. William Regal ☐
C. Tajiri ☐

Q55. Who won the Gimmick Battle Royal at *WrestleMania X-7?*

A. Iron Sheik ☐
B. Kamala ☐
C. The Goon ☐

Q56. Where did *WrestleMania X-7* take place?

A. Houston, Texas ☐
B. New York, New York ☐
C. Calgary, Alberta ☐

Q57. Who defeated William Regal for the Intercontinental Championship at *WrestleMania X8?*

A. Rob Van Dam ☐
B. Christian ☐
C. Chris Jericho ☐

Q58. Who became the Undisputed WWE Champion at *WrestleMania X8?*

A. Chris Jericho ☐
B. Triple H ☐
C. John Cena ☐

Q59. Who attempted to capture the European Championship at *WrestleMania X8?*

A. Christian ☐
B. British Bulldog ☐
C. Edge ☐

Q60. Who is this Superstar that came close to ending Undertaker's undefeated streak at *WrestleMania X8?*

A. Triple H ☐
B. Shawn Michaels ☐
C. Ric Flair ☐

Answers – 51-C, 52-A, 53-A, 54-B, 55-A, 56-A, 57-A, 58-B, 59-B, 60-C

WWE WRESTLE MANIA

MARCH 28, 1999

MATCH CARD

Triple Threat Match for the Hardcore Championship
Hardcore Holly def. Billy Gunn and Al Snow to become champion

World Tag Team Championship Match
Owen Hart and Jeff Jarrett w/ Debra def. Test and D-Lo Brown w/ Ivory to retain

Brawl 4 All
Butterbean def. Bart Gunn by knockout

Referee Match
Mankind def. Big Show by DQ to become referee for main event

Fatal Four Way Match for the Intercontinental Championship
Road Dogg def. Ken Shamrock, Val Venis and Goldust w/ Blue Meanie and Ryan Shamrock to retain

Kane def. Triple H by DQ

Women's Championship Match
Sable def. Tori

European Championship Match
Shane McMahon w/ Test def. X-Pac to retain

Hell in a Cell Match
Undertaker w/ Paul Bearer def. Big Boss Man

WWE Championship Match
Stone Cold Steve Austin def. The Rock to become new champion

DID YOU KNOW...

Stone Cold defeated The Rock to win the WWE Championship at *WrestleMania XV* - making him the first man ever to win the WWE Championship at consecutive *WrestleMania* events (he toppled Shawn Michaels for the Championship one year earlier).

WRESTLEMANIA 2000

APRIL 2, 2000

MATCH CARD

Big Boss Man and Bull Buchanan def. D-Lo Brown and The Godfather w/ Ice-T

Hardcore Battle Royal
Hardcore Holly was the final winner in the Hardcore Championship Battle Royal that also included Tazz, Kaientei, Mean Street Posse, The Headbangers, Viscera, The Acolytes and Crash Holly

Test and Albert w/ Trish Stratus def. Al Snow and Steve Blackman, w/ Chester McCheeserton

Ladder Match for the World Tag Team Championship
Edge and Christian def. the Dudleys and Hardy Boyz to become new champions

Catfight
Terri def. The Kat

Too Cool and Chyna def. The Radicalz

Triple Threat Match for the Intercontinental and European Championships
Chris Benoit pinned Chris Jericho to win the Intercontinental Championship; Chris Jericho pinned Chris Benoit to become European Champion; Kurt Angle was never pinned but lost both Championships

Kane and Rikishi def. Road Dogg and X-Pac

Fatal Four Way Elimination Match for the WWE Championship
Triple H w/ Stephanie McMahon def. The Rock w/ Mr. McMahon, Mick Foley w/ Linda McMahon and Big Show w/ Shane McMahon to retain

DID YOU KNOW...

Triple H's win in the main event of *WrestleMania 2000* was the first time a fan favourite did not emerge from a *WrestleMania a winner.*

Hardcore Holly emerged from *WrestleMania 2000* as the Hardcore Champion. It was the second consecutive *WrestleMania* Championship for him.

No 9 — ULTIMATE WARRIOR

Statistics...

Name:
Ultimate Warrior

Height:
6-foot-2

Weight:
275 pounds

From:
Parts Unknown

Signature Move:
Warrior Splash

WrestleMania Record

March 27, 1988 – *WrestleMania IV:* Ultimate Warrior defeated Hercules in his pay-per-view debut.

April 2, 1989 – *WrestleMania V:* Rick Rude defeated Ultimate Warrior for the Intercontinental Championship.

April 1, 1990 – *WrestleMania VI:* Ultimate Warrior defeated Hulk Hogan to become WWE Champion and retain the Intercontinental Championship.

March 24, 1991 – *WrestleMania VII:* Ultimate Warrior defeated Randy Savage in a "Retirement" match.

April 5, 1992 – *WrestleMania VIII:* Ultimate Warrior made a surprise return, helping Hulk Hogan during an attack from Sid and Papa Shango.

March 31, 1996 – *WrestleMania XII:* Ultimate Warrior defeated Hunter Hearst-Helmsley.

TRIPLE H — No 8

WrestleMania Record

March 31, 1996 – *WrestleMania XII:* Ultimate Warrior def. Hunter Hearst-Helmsley.

March 23, 1997 - *WrestleMania 13:* Hunter Hearst Helmsley w/Chyna def. Goldust w/Marlena.

March 29, 1998 – *WrestleMania XIV:* Triple H beat Owen Hart to retain the European Championship.

March 28, 1999 – *WrestleMania XV:* Kane beat Triple H by DQ (Chyna turned on Kane and rejoined Triple H and DX).

April 2, 2000 – *WrestleMania 2000:* Triple H def. The Rock, Mick Foley & Big Show in a Fatal Four Way Match.

April 1, 2001 – *WrestleMania X-7:* Undertaker def. Triple H.

March 17, 2002 – *WrestleMania X8:* Triple H def. Chris Jericho to become the Undisputed WWE Champion!

March 30, 2003 – *WrestleMania XIX:* Triple H def. Booker T to retain the World Heavyweight Championship.

March 14, 2004 – *WrestleMania XX:* Chris Benoit beat Triple H and Shawn Michaels to capture the World Heavyweight Championship.

April 3, 2005 – *WrestleMania 21:* Batista def. Triple H to capture the World Heavyweight Championship.

April 2, 2006 – *WrestleMania 22:* John Cena def. Triple H to retain the WWE Championship!

March 30, 2008 – *WrestleMania XXIV:* Randy Orton def. Triple H and John Cena in a Triple Threat Match to retain the WWE Championship.

April 5, 2009 – *WrestleMania XXV:* Triple H def. Randy Orton using the sledge-hammer to retain the WWE Championship.

Statistics...

Name:
Triple H

Height:
6-foot-4

Weight:
255 pounds

From:
Greenwich, CT

Signature Move:
Pedigree

THE BIG WRESTLEMANIA QUIZ PART VII

Only two more rounds to go! This could be the difference between becoming World Champion or getting fired!

Q61. In which city did *WrestleMania XIX* take place?

A. Seattle ☐
B. Chicago ☐
C. London ☐

Q62. Who faced Mr McMahon at *WrestleMania XIX?*

A. Hulk Hogan ☐
B. Triple H ☐
C. Shawn Michaels ☐

Q63. Who did Shawn Michaels defeat at *WrestleMania XIX?*

A. Triple H ☐
B. Chris Jericho ☐
C. Kane ☐

Q64. Who is this Superstar that competed for the World Tag Team Championship at *WrestleMania XIX?*

A. Eddie Guerrero ☐
B. Vickie Guerrero ☐
C. Chavo Guerrero ☐

Q65. Which championship did John Cena win at *WrestleMania XX?*

A. Intercontinental ☐
B. United States ☐
C. Hardcore ☐

Q66. Who turned on Chris Jericho costing him the match at *WrestleMania XX?*

A. Trish Stratus ☐
B. Christian ☐
C. Layla ☐

Q67. What kind of match did Big Show compete in at *WrestleMania 21?*

A. TLC ☐
B. Sumo ☐
C. Boxing ☐

Q68. Who won the Money in The Bank Ladder Match at *WrestleMania 21?*

A. Shelton Benjamin ☐
B. CM Punk ☐
C. Edge ☐

Q69. Who defeated Triple H at *WrestleMania 21?*

A. Edge ☐
B. Undertaker ☐
C. Batista ☐

Q70. Who is this Superstar that had her head shaved as a result of losing her match at *WrestleMania XX?*

A. Lita ☐
B. Trish Stratus ☐
C. Molly Holly ☐

Answers – 61-A, 62-B, 63-B, 64-C, 65-B, 66-A, 67-B, 68-C, 69-C, 70-C

UNDERTAKER
VS
SHAWN MICHAELS

"This is truly going to be a match for the ages! This man, Shawn Michaels is looking to end Undertaker's undefeated streak at *WrestleMania* and prove once and for all that he is the Showstopper!"

"Undertaker has said in past weeks that HBK has opened up the gates of hell."

"And straight out of those gates, here comes Undertaker! There is no doubt in my mind that Undertaker is one of the most dominating forces in the history of WWE!"

"He is a master of the mind game! You have to wonder whether he has gotten inside Shawn Michaels' head!"

"The referee has rung the bell and this match is underway!"

"And look at this! Undertaker is taking HBK back to school! Old School that is!"

"Undertaker immediately shows that he has the advantage when it comes to strength!"

"Shawn Michaels comes back with some offence of his own, going to work on Undertaker's midsection!"

"Shawn Michaels has Undertaker locked into the Figure Four Leglock! Will Undertaker submit here?"

"Undertaker breaks the hold and comes back with some offence of his own. Just look at the elevation he got on that leg drop!"

"Undertaker has Shawn Michaels locked into Hells Gate! This submission move has put away so many opponents before now!"

"Somehow, HBK managed to escape the hold and is looking to go high risk here! HBK with a moonsault to the outside!"

"Undertaker saw him coming though and swiped him away! Undertaker is such a ring general. He scouted that move and took appropriate action!"

"Undertaker looks like he is about to go airborne himself!"

"Undertaker just leapt clear over the top rope! It looked like Shawn Michaels pulled that camera man in front of him and used him as a shield!"

"Undertaker's face and head just bounced off the mat on the outside! Undertaker may be injured here!"

"HBK is just waiting for Undertaker to get back in the ring! He is tuning up the band and that can mean only one thing!"

"HBK goes for the Sweet Chin Music but Undertaker counters with a devastating Chokeslam!"

"And Undertaker really caught HBK with that move! He is going for the pin. 1…2… HBK somehow manages to kick out!"

"HBK goes for another Sweet Chin Music! Undertaker saw it coming and blocked the attempt!"

"But HBK counters again and this time the kick is right on the button!"

"Undertaker is taking a page out of HBK's book here! He is going for the top rope elbow drop! Wow! Shawn Michaels somehow rolled out of the way!"

"HBK goes for the pin! But Undertaker has caught him by the throat and delivers yet another Chokeslam!"

"Both men are down! Look at the look on Undertaker's face! What will it take to win this match?"

"Undertaker catches a boot to the face in the corner!"

"HBK has climbed to the top and is going to show Undertaker how it should be done!"

"Shawn Michaels just delivered a huge elbow drop right to the heart of Undertaker! Go for the pin Shawn!"

"HBK wants to make sure Undertaker is finished off and has gone back to the top rope! He is trying for a moonsault!"

"Undertaker caught him in midair! Undertaker has HBK set up for the Tombstone Piledriver!"

"Undertaker connected! He is going for the pin! 1...2...3! It's over! Undertaker has defeated Shawn Michaels and kept the streak alive!"

"Both of these Superstars gave their all in this match, but as the bell sounds, only one man can be victorious!"

MATCH CARD

Intercontinental Championship Match
Chris Jericho def. William Regal to retain

Bradshaw, Faarooq and Tazz def. Right To Censor

Triple Threat Match for the Hardcore Championship
Kane def. Big Show and Raven to become new champion

European Championship Match
Eddie Guerrero def. Test to become new champion

Kurt Angle def. Chris Benoit

Women's Championship Match
Chyna def. Ivory to become the new champion

Street Fight
Shane McMahon def. Mr. McMahon (Mick Foley was special guest referee)

Tables, Ladders and Chairs Match for the World Tag Team Championship
Edge and Christian def. the Dudleys and Hardy Boyz to become new champions

Gimmick Battle Royal
Iron Sheik def. Brother Love, Bushwhackers, Jim Cornette, Doink, Duke 'The Dumpster' Droese, Earthquake, Gobbledy Gooker, The Goon, Michael Hayes, Hillbilly Jim, Kamala, Kim Chee, One Man Gang, Repo Man, Sgt Slaughter, Tugboat and Nikolai Volkoff

Undertaker def. Triple H

WWE Championship Match
Stone Cold Steve Austin def. The Rock to become new champion

DID YOU KNOW...

The 67,925 fans at the Astrodome established a new all-time record for that venue.

Stone Cold vs. The Rock is only the second match to be a main event at two *WrestleMania* events - Bret Hart vs. Yokozuna highlighted *WrestleMania IX & X.*

WRESTLEMANIA X8

MARCH 17, 2002

MATCH CARD

Intercontinental Championship Match
Rob Van Dam def. William Regal to become new champion

European Championship Match
Diamond Dallas Page def. Christian to retain

Hardcore Championship Match
Spike Dudley, The Hurricane, Mighty Molly, Maven and lastly Christian all scored pinfalls to become Hardcore Champion during the night

Kurt Angle def. Kane

Undertaker def. Ric Flair

Edge def. Booker T

Stone Cold Steve Austin def. Scott Hall w/ Kevin Nash

Fatal Four Way Elimination Match for the World Tag Team Championship
Billy and Chuck def. The Hardy Boyz, the APA and the Dudleys

Icon vs Icon Match
The Rock def. Hollywood Hulk Hogan

Triple Threat Match for the Women's Championship
Jazz def. Lita and Trish Stratus to retain

Undisputed WWE Championship Match
Triple H def. Chris Jericho w/ Stephanie McMahon

DID YOU KNOW...

Hollywood Hulk Hogan returned to *WrestleMania* at *WrestleMania X8* when he took on The Rock. It was Hogan's first *WrestleMania* match since *WrestleMania IX*.

Undertaker defeated Ric Flair at *WrestleMania X8*, taking his undefeated *WrestleMania* record to 10-0.

No 7 — RIC FLAIR

Statistics...

Name:
Ric Flair

Height:
6-foot-1

Weight:
243 pounds

From:
Charlotte, NC

Signature Move:
Figure-Four Leglock

WrestleMania Record

April 5, 1992 – *WrestleMania VIII:* Randy 'Macho Man' Savage def. Ric Flair for the WWE Championship.

March 17, 2002 – *WrestleMania X8:* Ric Flair is def. by Undertaker.

March 14, 2004 – *WrestleMania XX:* Evolution (Randy Orton/Batista/Ric Flair) beat Mick Foley and The Rock.

April 2, 2006 – *WrestleMania 22:* RVD beat Shelton Benjamin, Flair, Finlay, Lashley and Matt Hardy in a Money in the Bank Ladder Match.

April 1, 2007 – *WrestleMania 23:* Ric Flair and Carlito def. Gregory Helms and Chavo Guerrero in a special Pre-WrestleMania Non-televised Match .

March 30, 2008 – *WrestleMania XXIV:* Shawn Michaels def. 'Nature Boy' Ric Flair in a Career-threatening Match.

April 5, 2009 – *WrestleMania XXV:* Chris Jericho def. Legends (Jimmy Snuka, Ricky Steamboat and Roddy Piper w/Ric Flair).

STONE COLD STEVE AUSTIN — No 6

WrestleMania Record

March 31, 1996 - *WrestleMania XII:* 'The Ringmaster' Steve Austin w/ Ted DiBiase def. Savio Vega.

March 23, 1997 - *WrestleMania 13:* Bret 'Hit Man' Hart def. Stone Cold Steve Austin in a 'Submission' match.

March 29, 1998 - *WrestleMania XIV:* Stone Cold Steve Austin def. Shawn Michaels.

March 28, 1999 - *WrestleMania XV:* Stone Cold Steve Austin def. The Rock (of the Corporation).

April 1, 2001 - *WrestleMania X-7:* Stone Cold Steve Austin beat The Rock in a 'NO DQ' match.

WrestleMania X8: Stone Cold Steve Austin def. Scott Hall.

March 30, 2003 - *WrestleMania XIX:* The Rock def. Stone Cold Steve Austin, nailing three Rock Bottoms.

March 14, 2004 - *WrestleMania XX:* Stone Cold Steve Austin STUNNED both Goldberg and Brock Lesnar.

April 3, 2005 - *WrestleMania 21:* Roddy Piper had Stone Cold Steve Austin as his guest in Piper's Pit.

April 1, 2007 - *WrestleMania 23:* Bobby Lashley w/Donald Trump def. Umaga w/Mr McMahon in a Hair vs. Hair match. Stone Cold Steve Austin was the referee.

April 5, 2008- WrestleMania 25: Stone Cold Steve Austin is honoured among the WWE Hall of Fame Class of 2009.

Statistics...

Name:
Stone Cold Steve Austin

Height:
6-foot-2

Weight:
252 pounds

From:
Victoria, TX

Signature Move:
Stone Cold Stunner

ARRIVE. RAISE HELL. LEAVE.

THE BIG WRESTLEMANIA

QUIZ PART VIII

ere it is, the final round of the *WrestleMania* Quiz! This is your last chance to prove you have what it
kes to be a WWE Champion. Now it's time to add up your scores and find out what championship you
ave won! 0-20 'You're Fired!', 20-30 United States Champion!, 30-40 Intercontinental Champion!,
0-50 World Heavyweight Champion!, 50-60 WWE Champion!, 60-70 Undisputed Champion of the World

Q71. Who did Kane team with at *WrestleMania 22?*

A. Big Show

B. Undertaker

C. The Great Khali

Q72. What kind of match did Undertaker compete in at *WrestleMania 22?*

A. Casket Match

B. Hell In A Cell

C. Ladder Match

Q73. Where did *WrestleMania 23* take place?

A. Detroit, Michigan

B. New York, New York

C. Dallas, Texas

Q74. Who is this Diva that lost in a pillow fight match at *WrestleMania 22?*

A. Candice

B. Layla

C. Maria

Q75. Who represented Mr McMahon in the Hair vs Hair Match at *WrestleMania 23?*

A. Umaga

B. Big Show

C. Edge

Q76. Who did John Cena face at *WrestleMania 23?*

A. Triple H

B. Shawn Michaels

C. Edge

Q77. Who won the Playboy Bunny-Mania Lumberjills Match at *WrestleMania XXIV?*

A. Beth Phoenix

B. Melina

C. Candice

Q78. How many matches took place at *WrestleMania XXIV?*

A. 8

B. 9

C. 10

Q79. Who defeated Edge at *WrestleMania XXIV?*

A. Undertaker

B. John Cena

C. Triple H

Q80. Who is this Superstar that competed in the Money In The Bank Ladder Match at *WrestleMania XXIV?*

A. Edge

B. CM Punk

C. John Morrison

Answers – 71-A, 72-A, 73-A, 74-A, 75-A, 76-B, 77-A, 78-B, 79-A, 80-C.

TRIPLE TREAT MATCH

EDGE vs BIG SHOW vs JOHN CENA

"This match will be for the World Heavyweight Championship! Here comes the reigning champion now, 'The Rated R Superstar', Edge!"

"This match is a three-way match and here is one of Edge's opponents, the seven foot-plus, Big Show!"

"What an entrance from the former champion, John Cena! I have never seen anything like it!"

"All three men are sizing each other up, and the match is about to begin."

"Cena drives Edge face first into the mat! Edge might be eating through a straw after that move!"

"Big Show goes straight after John Cena! It was only a few weeks ago that John Cena was knocked out at the hands of Big Show."

"Big Show is on the attack and takes down both John Cena and Edge! I don't think even those two great Superstars can match Big Show for power!"

"Big Show is showing some of that power here with this move. He just hoisted Edge above his head as if he were a rag doll!"

"Big Show has Edge in the corner and is about to deliver one of those giant sized chops! Wow! You could hear that impact reverberate around the entire arena!"

"John Cena is back in the ring and has Edge set up for the Attitude Adjustment!"

"Big Show just saved Edge from the Attitude Adjustment by kicking John Cena in the chest with his massive boot!"

"Now Big Show is on the offensive! A huge sidewalk slam! The whole ring shook with that impact!"

"Chavo Guerrero, who's ringside with Vickie Guerrero, just grabbed John Cena's leg and has received an Attitude Adjustment for his trouble!"

"Cena with the Five Knuckle Shuffle!"

"Big Show is tied up in the ropes! This gives Cena a great chance to take out Edge!"

"Edge was looking to hit John Cena with the spear but he accidentally took out his wife, Vickie Guerrero instead."

"Big Show is still tied up on the ropes! He is shouting at the referee to untangle him!"

"Big Show has escaped! Now Edge and John Cena have to deal with a very angry giant!"

"Big Show has John Cena in the corner! A huge chop from Big Show!"

"Look at that! Big Show just crushed both John Cena and Edge up against the turnbuckle!"

91

"Big Show is looking for a double Chokeslam here!"

"Edge just received a giant sized Chokeslam! Somehow John Cena managed to counter the move!"

"John Cena and Edge have realised that they need to work together to take out Big Show."

"Big Show is on the outside! Edge with the flying clothesline! Big Show is down!"

"A huge double suplex! How strong are John Cena and Edge!"

"And a double clothesline sends Big Show over the top rope!"

"Now John Cena has gone to the top rope! Big Show just pushed him off the turnbuckle!"

"Edge caught Cena in mid-air with the spear!"

"And now Edge is trying to choke out Big Show!"

"Edge escaped but here is a huge Attitude Adjustment to Big Show!"

"Oh My God! John Cena has both Big Show and Edge set up for a double Attitude Adjustment!"

"Edge goes for the spear but Cena counters with another Attitude Adjustment on top of Big Show! Cena is going for the pin! 1...2...3! Cena has won it!"

"John Cena has recaptured the World Heavyweight Championship!"

MATCH CARD

Cruiserweight Championship Match
Matt Hardy def. Rey Mysterio to retain

Handicap Match
Undertaker def. Big Show and A-Train

Triple Threat Match for the Women's Championship
Trish Stratus def. Jazz and Victoria to become new champion

Triple Threat Match for the WWE Tag Team Championship
Team Angle def. Los Guerreros and Chris Benoit and Rhyno to retain

Shawn Michaels def. Chris Jericho

Cat Fight
Stacy Keibler, Torrie Wilson and the Miller Light Cat Fight girls went to a no contest

World Heavyweight Championship Match
Triple H w/ Ric Flair def. Booker T to retain

Street Fight
Hulk Hogan def. Mr McMahon

The Rock def. Stone Cold Steve Austin

WWE Championship Match
Brock Lesnar def. Kurt Angle to become the new champion

DID YOU KNOW...

WrestleMania XIX was the first for Rey Mysterio, Victoria, Shelton Benjamin, Charlie Haas, Chavo Guerrero and Brock Lesnar.

Hulk Hogan picked up his first *WrestleMania* win since 1993.

Limp Bizkit performed their hit song *Rollin*, for Undertaker's entrance.

Title: Where it All Begins... Again
Location: New York City, NY
Arena: Madison Square Garden
Attendance: 20,000

MARCH 14, 2004

WWE
WRESTLEMANIA XX

MATCH CARD

United States Championship Match
John Cena def. Big Show to become the new champion

Fatal Four Way Match for the World Tag Team Championship
Booker T and Rob Van Dam def. La Resistance, Mark Jindrak and Garrison Cade and the Dudleys to retain

Christian def. Chris Jericho w/ Trish Stratus

Handicap Match
Randy Orton, Batista and Ric Flair def. The Rock and Mick Foley

Playboy Evening Gown Match
Sable and Torrie Wilson def. Stacy Keibler and Miss Jackie

Cruiserweight Open for the Cruiserweight Championship
Ultimo Dragon def. Shannon Moore; Jamie Noble def. Ultimo Dragon; Jamie Noble def. Funaki; Jamie Noble def. Nunzio;
Billy Kidman def. Jamie Noble; Rey Mysterio def. Billy Kidman; Rey Mysterio def. Tajiri; Chavo Guerrero w/ Chavo
Classic def. Rey Mysterio to retain

Goldberg def. Brock Lesnar (Stone Cold was special guest referee)

Fatal Four Way Match for the WWE Tag Team Championship
Scotty 2 Hotty and Rikishi def. Basham Brothers, World's Greatest Tag Team and APA to retain

Women's Championship Match
Victoria def. Molly Holly to retain

WWE Championship Match
Eddie Guerrero def. Kurt Angle to retain

Undertaker w/ Paul Bearer def. Kane

Triple Threat Match for the World Heavyweight Championship
Chris Benoit def. Triple H and Shawn Michaels to become new champion

DID YOU KNOW...

WrestleMania XX was the third time Madison Square Garden hosted the event (*WrestleMania I and X* were the others).

The United States Championship was defended for the first time in *WrestleMania* history when Big Show defended against John Cena at *WrestleMania XX*.

No 5

BRET 'HIT MAN' HART™

Statistics...

Name:
Bret 'Hit Man' Hart

Height:
6-foot-0

Weight:
234 pounds

From:
Calgary, AB

Signature Move:
The Sharpshooter

WrestleMania Record

April 2, 1986 – *WrestleMania 2:* Last man eliminated in a 20 Man Battle Royal.

March 27, 1987 – *WrestleMania III:* The Hart Foundation & Danny Davis def. The British Bulldogs & Tito Santana.

March 27, 1988 – *WrestleMania IV:* Last wrestler to be eliminated by Bad News Brown Battle Royal.

April 2, 1989 – *WrestleMania V:* The Hart Foundation def. the Honky Tonk Man & Greg Valentine.

April 1, 1990 – WrestleMania VI: The Hart Foundation def. the Bolshivics in just 19 seconds.

March 24, 1991 – *WrestleMania VII:* The Nasty Boys def. The Hart Foundation to win the Tag Team Championship.

April 5, 1992 – *WrestleMania VIII:* Def. Roddy Piper.

April 4, 1993 – *WrestleMania IX:* Yokozuna def Bret 'Hit Man' Hart.

March 20, 1994 – *WrestleMania X:* Owen Hart def. brother Bret 'Hit Man' Hart. Bret 'Hit Man' Hart later beat Yokozuna to capture the WWE Championship.

April 2, 1995 – *WrestleMania XI:* Def. Bob Backlund in a hard fought 'I Quit' Match.

March 31, 1996 – *WrestleMania XII:* Shawn Michaels def. Bret 'Hit Man' Hart.

March 23, 1997 – *WrestleMania 13:* Defeated Stone Cold Steve Austin.

RICKY 'THE DRAGON' STEAMBOAT™ No 4

WrestleMania Record

March 31, 1985 – *WrestleMania:* Ricky 'The Dragon' Steamboat defeated Matt Bourne.

April 7, 1986 – *WrestleMania II:* Ricky 'The Dragon' Steamboat defeated Hercules Hernandez.

March 29, 1987 – *WrestleMania III:* Ricky 'The Dragon' Steamboat defeated Randy 'Macho Man' Savage to win the Intercontinental Championship.

March 28, 1988 – *WrestleMania IV:* Greg Valentine defeated Ricky 'The Dragon' Steamboat in the first round of the WWE Championship Tournament.

April 5, 2009 – *WrestleMania 25:* Chris Jericho defeated Legends (Jimmy Snuka and Ricky Steamboat and Roddy Piper w/ Ric Flair).

Statistics...

Name:
Ricky 'The Dragon' Steamboat

Height:
5-foot-10

Weight:
235 pounds

From:
Honolulu, HI

Signature Move:
Flying Bodypress

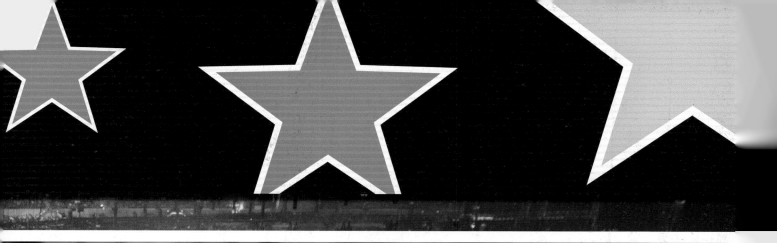

No 3

SHAWN MICHAELS®

Statistics...

Name:
Shawn Michaels

Height:
6-foot-1

Weight:
225 pounds

From:
San Antonio, TX

Signature Move:
Sweet Chin Music

WrestleMania Record

April 2, 1989 – *WrestleMania V:*
The Twin Towers def The Rockers.
April 1, 1990 – *WrestleMania VI:*
The Orient Express def The Rockers.
March 24, 1991 - *WrestleMania VII:*
The Rockers defeated Barbarian, Haku & Bobby Heenan.
April 5, 1992 – *WrestleMania VIII:*
Shawn Michaels & Sensational Sherri def 'El Matador' Tito Santana.
April 4, 1993 – *WrestleMania IX:*
Tatanka defeated Shawn Michaels.
March 20, 1994 – *WrestleMania X:*
Razor Ramon def Shawn Michaels.
April 2, 1995 – *WrestleMania XI:*
Diesel defeated Shawn Michaels.
March 31, 1996 – *WrestleMania XII:*
Shawn Michaels def Bret 'Hit Man' Hart.
March 23, 1997 – *WrestleMania 13:*
Shawn Michaels gave commentary.

March 29, 1998 – *WrestleMania XIV:*
Stone Cold Steve Austin defeated Shawn Michaels.

March 28, 1999 – *WrestleMania XV:*
Shawn Michaels guest appearance.
March 30, 2003 – *WrestleMania XIX:*
Shawn Michaels def Chris Jericho.
March 14, 2004 – *WrestleMania XX:*
Chris Benoit def Shawn Michaels & Triple H.
April 3, 2005 – *WrestleMania 21:*
Kurt Angle def Shawn Michaels.
April 2, 2006 – *WrestleMania 22:*
Shawn Michaels def Mr McMahon.
April 1, 2007 – *WrestleMania 23:*
John Cena def Shawn Michaels.
March 30, 2008 - *WrestleMania XXIV:*
Shawn Michaels def Ric Flair.
April 5, 2009 – *WrestleMania XXV:*
Undertaker def Shawn Michaels.

HULK HOGAN™

No 2

WrestleMania Record

March 31, 1985 – *WrestleMania:*
Hulk Hogan and Mr. T w/Jimmy Snuka def. Roddy Piper and Paul Orndorff w/Bob Orton.
April 5, 1986 – *WrestleMania 2:*
Hulk Hogan def. King Kong Bundy in a Steel Cage match.
March 29, 1987 – *WrestleMania III:*
Hulk Hogan def. Andre The Giant w/Bobby Heenan.
March 27, 1988 – *WrestleMania IV:*
Hulk Hogan and Andre The Giant were both disqualified during WWE Championship Tournament.
April 5, 1989 – *WrestleMania V:*
Hulk Hogan def. Randy 'Macho Man' Savage.
April 1, 1990 – *WrestleMania VI:*
Ultimate Warrior def. Hulk Hogan.

March 24, 1991 – *WrestleMania VII:*
Hulk Hogan def. Sgt. Slaughterp.
April 5, 1992 – *WrestleMania VIII:*
Hulk Hogan def. Sid Justice w/ Harvey Wippleman by DQ when Papa Shango interfered.
April 4, 1993 – *WrestleMania IX:*
Money Inc. (Ted DiBiase and IRS) def. Hulk Hogan and Brutus Beefcake w/Jimmy Hart by DQ.
March 17, 2002 – *WrestleMania X8:*
The Rock def. Hulk Hogan.
March 30, 2003 – *WrestleMania XIX:*
Hulk Hogan beat Mr McMahon in a Street Fight despite the shocking interference from Roddy Piper!
April 3, 2005 – *WrestleMania 21:*
Hulk Hogan saved Eugene from a beat down by Muhammad Hassan and Khrosrow Daivari.

Statistics...

Name:
Hulk Hogan

Height:
6-foot-6

Weight:
302 pounds

From:
Venice Beach, CA

Signature Move:
Leg Drop

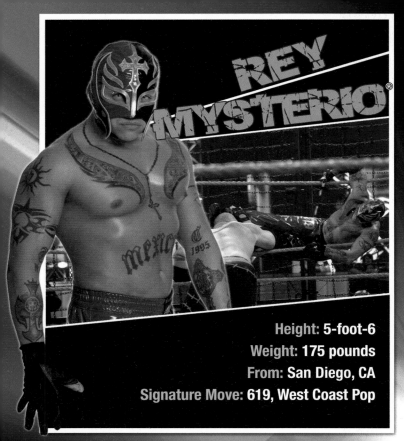

REY MYSTERIO

Height: **5-foot-6**
Weight: **175 pounds**
From: **San Diego, CA**
Signature Move: **619, West Coast Pop**

CM PUNK

Height: **6-foot-1**
Weight: **222 pounds**
From: **Chicago, IL**
Signature Move: **GTS (Go To Sleep)**

EDGE

Height: **6-foot-5**
Weight: **250 pounds**
From: **Toronto, ON**
Signature Move: **Spear**

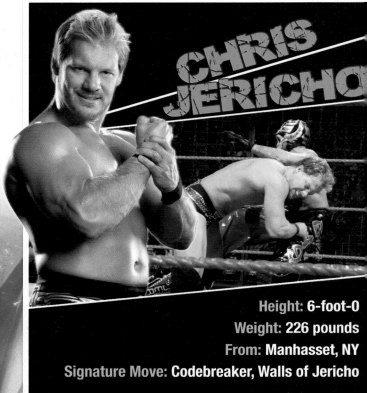

CHRIS JERICHO

Height: **6-foot-0**
Weight: **226 pounds**
From: **Manhasset, NY**
Signature Move: **Codebreaker, Walls of Jericho**

SMACK DOWN

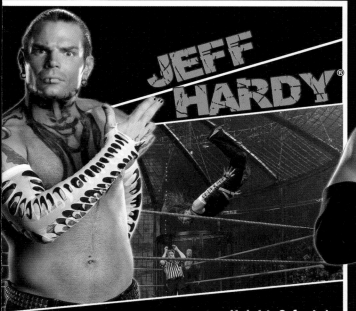

JEFF HARDY

Height: 6-foot-1
Weight: 225 pounds
From: Cameron, NC
Signature Move: Swanton Bomb,
Whisper in the Wind, Twist of Fate

KANE

Height: 7-foot-0
Weight: 323 pounds
From: Parts Unknown
Signature Move: Chokeslam

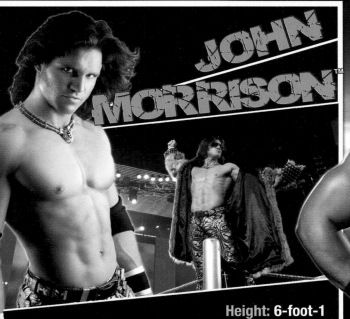

JOHN MORRISON

Height: 6-foot-1
Weight: 219 pounds
From: Los Angeles, CA
Signature Move: Snapshot, Moonlight Drive

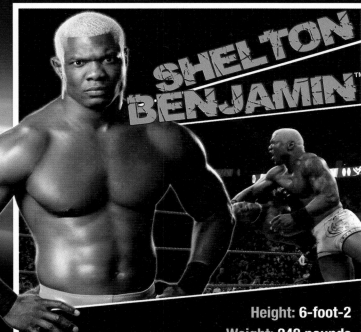

SHELTON BENJAMIN

Height: 6-foot-2
Weight: 248 pounds
From: Orangeburg, SC
Signature Move: T-bone Suplex

PROFILES

APRIL 3, 2005

MATCH CARD

Rey Mysterio def. Eddie Guerrero

Money in the Bank Ladder Match
Edge def. Chris Benoit, Shelton Benjamin, Chris Jericho, Christian and Kane

Interpromotional Match
Undertaker def. Randy Orton

Women's Championship Match
Trish Stratus def. Christy Hemme w/ Lita to retain

Interpromotional Match
Kurt Angle def. Shawn Michaels

Sumo Match
Akebono def. Big Show

WWE Championship Match
John Cena def. JBL to become the new champion

World Heavyweight Championship Match
Batista def. Triple H to become the new champion

DID YOU KNOW...

Big Show faced Akebono in the first Sumo Match in WWE history.

Undertaker's *WrestleMania* record went up to an amazing 13-0.

The WWE and World Heavyweight Championship changed hands as John Cena defeated JBL and Batista defeated Triple H, respectively.

Title: Big Time
Location: Chicago, IL
Arena: All-State Arena
Attendance: 17,155

BIG TIME

WWE

WRESTLEMANIA

22

MATCH CARD

World Tag Team Championship Match
World Tag Team Champions Kane and Big Show def. Chris Masters and Carlito

Money in the Bank Ladder Match
RVD def. Ric Flair, Finlay, Shelton Benjamin, Bobby Lashley, and Matt Hardy

United States Championship Match
JBL def. Chris Benoit

Hardcore Match
Edge def. Mick Foley

Handicap Match
Boogeyman def. Booker T and Sharmell

Women's Championship Match
Mickie James def. Trish Stratus (new Women's Champion)

Casket Match
Undertaker def. Mark Henry

No Holds Barred Match
Shawn Michaels def. Mr. McMahon

Triple Threat Match for the World Heavyweight Championship
Rey Mysterio def. Kurt Angle and Randy Orton

Playboy Pillow Fight
Torrie Wilson def. Candice Michelle

WWE Championship Match
WWE Champion John Cena def. Triple H

DID YOU KNOW...

Michelle Williams sang
America the Beautiful to open.

P.O.D played live and performed
Rey Mysterio's entrance theme!

WrestleMania 22 was the first
WrestleMania not to feature the
winner of the *Royal Rumble* in
the *WrestleMania* final match
since 1999.

WWE CHAMPIONSHIP MATCH
TRIPLE H VS RANDY ORTON

"Well we are all set for the main event of the evening! This man, Randy Orton will take on Triple H for the WWE Championship!"

"Orton looks totally focused! 'The Viper' means business tonight!"

"And here comes the champion, Triple H! What an entrance, smashing through that glass wall!"

"This match is about more than the championship for Triple H. When you think back to what Randy Orton did to his wife just a few weeks ago, I certainly would not want to be in Orton's shoes!"

"Just look at the intensity on the face of the champion!"

"Orton does not look intimidated at all! He knows Triple H inside and out! These two were partners at one point!"

"The match is underway and Orton takes Triple H down!"

"Orton just hit the RKO! Out of nowhere, Orton hit his signature move!"

"What is Orton thinking here? He may be looking to punt Triple H in the head!"

"Orton gave Triple H time to recover! That could be a huge mistake for the challenger!"

"Triple H is now in control as he delivers a boot to Randy Orton's midsection!"

"Triple H using some interesting offence here. He almost decapitated Orton with that move!"

"A huge knee to the side of Orton's face from Triple H!"

"Randy Orton is back in control! The momentum of this match keeps swinging back and forth!"

"Now it is Orton delivering a knee to Triple H's face! Orton sure does have a mean streak!"

"Triple H looks as though he may be out cold! And those fierce right hand shots from Orton are not going to help his situation!"

"Randy Orton is trying to wear the champion down with a rear naked chin lock."

"Randy Orton may be looking to slingshot Triple H over the top rope here!"

"This is a smart move by Orton. If he can keep Triple H down on the mat, then he remains in control of the match."

"But look at this! Randy Orton quickly counters with a modified backbreaker! Orton is just so dangerous!"

"Triple H fires back with a huge clothesline that knocks the challenger down!"

"Orton tried for another kick to Triple H's head but the champion caught his foot and has just dumped him over the top rope!"

"Orton with the guillotine DDT! Triple H's skull just bounced off the mats at ringside!"

"Orton just nailed a groggy Triple H with a huge right hand! I think Triple H may be unconscious!"

"Triple H was looking to Pedigree Randy Orton through the announce table but Orton has countered with a backdrop onto the table!"

"Orton is looking under the ring, what has he found?"

"It's Triple H's sledgehammer! Orton is going to try and end Triple H's career here tonight!"

"Orton goes to nail Triple H but the champion ducks out of the way and hits Orton with a sledgehammer shot of his own!"

"Triple H is going for the Pedigree! If he hits this move the match should be over!"

"Triple H hooks the leg and makes the cover! 1...2...3! Triple H has defeated Randy Orton!"

"Triple H has found some form of retribution for all the terrible acts that Randy Orton performed on his family. What an amazing match!"

"Triple H has retained his championship and gained revenge for the entire McMahon family! That's it from *WrestleMania XXV*, we'll see you next time!"

WRESTLEMANIA 23

MATCH CARD

Money in the Bank Ladder Match
Mr. Kennedy def. Edge, CM Punk, King Booker (with Queen Sharmell), Jeff Hardy, Matt Hardy, Finlay and Randy Orton

The Great Khali def. Kane

United States Championship Match
Chris Benoit def. Montel Vontavious Porter

World Heavyweight Championship Match
Undertaker def. Batista

The ECW Originals (Tommy Dreamer, Sabu, The Sandman and Rob Van Dam) def.
The New Breed (Elijah Burke, Marcus Cor Von, Matt Striker and Kevin Thorn with Ariel)

Battle of the Billionaires
Hair vs Hair Match
Bobby Lashley (with Donald Trump) def. Umaga (with Mr McMahon and Armando Alejandro Estrada)
with Stone Cold Steve Austin as Special Guest Referee

Women's Championship Match
Melina def. Ashley

WWE Championship Match
John Cena def. Shawn Michaels

DID YOU KNOW...

Aretha Franklin opened reprising her role from 20 years earlier at *WrestleMania III*.

This was the fourth year the World Heavyweight Championship changed hands.

Undertaker's win made him the only Superstar in history to win both Championships at a *WrestleMania*.

MARCH 30, 2008

WrestleMania XXIV

MATCH CARD

Belfast Brawl
JBL def. **Finlay**

Money In The Bank Ladder Match
CM Punk def. **Chris Jericho, Carlito, MVP, Shelton Benjamin, John Morrison, and Mr. Kennedy**

Battle for Brand Supremacy
Batista def. **Umaga**

ECW Championship Match
Kane def. **Chavo Guerrero to become new champion**

Career Threatening Match
Shawn Michaels def. **Ric Flair**

BunnyMania Lumberjill Match
Beth Phoenix and Melina def. **Ashley and Maria**

Triple Threat Match for the WWE Championship
Randy Orton def. **John Cena and Triple H to retain**

The Biggest vs The Best
Floyd "Money" Mayweather def. **Big Show (Knockout)**

World Heavyweight Championship Match
Undertaker def. **Edge to become new champion**

No 1

UNDERTAKER ©

Statistics...

Name:
Undertaker

Height:
6-foot-10 1/2

Weight:
299 pounds

From:
Death Valley, CA

Signature Move:
Chokeslam,
Tombstone,
Last Ride

WrestleMania Record

March 24, 1991 – *WrestleMania VII*:
Undertaker & Paul Bearer defeated Jimmy 'Superfly' Snuka.

April 5, 1992 – *WrestleMania VIII*:
Undertaker & Paul Bearer defeated Jake 'The Snake' Roberts.

April 4, 1993 – *WrestleMania IX*:
Undertaker & Paul Bearer defeated Giant Gonzales w/Harvey Wippleman by DQ.

April 2, 1995 – *WrestleMania XI*:
Undertaker & Paul Bearer defeated King Kong Bundy & Ted DiBiase.

March 31, 1996 – *WrestleMania XII*:
Undertaker & Paul Bearer defeated 'Big Daddy Cool' Diesel in a Grudge match.

March 23, 1997 – *WrestleMania 13*:
Undertaker defeated Sycho Sid.

March 29, 1998 – *WrestleMania XIV*:
Undertaker defeated Kane & Paul Bearer.

March 28, 1999 – *WrestleMania XV*:
Undertaker defeated Big Bossman.

April 1, 2001 – *WrestleMania X-7*:
Undertaker defeated Triple H.

March 17, 2002 – *WrestleMania X8*:
Undertaker defeated 'Nature Boy' Ric Flair.

March 30, 2003 – *WrestleMania XIX*:
Undertaker beat Big Show and A-Train.

March 14, 2004 – *WrestleMania XX*:
Undertaker & Paul Bearer defeated Kane.

April 3, 2005 – *WrestleMania 21*:
Undertaker defeated Randy Orton.

April 2, 2006 – *WrestleMania 22*:
Undertaker defeated Mark Henry.

April 1, 2007 – *WrestleMania 23*:
Undertaker defeated Batista.

March 30, 2008 – *WrestleMania XXIV*:
Undertaker defeated Edge.

April 5, 2009 – *WrestleMania XXV*:
Undertaker defeated Shawn Michaels.